Giorgos Mpantes

Images in Electricity

Intellect and Senses

LAP LAMBERT Academic Publishing

Imprint

Any brand names and product names mentioned in this book are subject to trademark, brand or patent protection and are trademarks or registered trademarks of their respective holders. The use of brand names, product names, common names, trade names, product descriptions etc. even without a particular marking in this work is in no way to be construed to mean that such names may be regarded as unrestricted in respect of trademark and brand protection legislation and could thus be used by anyone.

Cover image: www.ingimage.com

Publisher:
LAP LAMBERT Academic Publishing
is a trademark of
International Book Market Service Ltd., member of OmniScriptum Publishing Group
17 Meldrum Street, Beau Bassin 71504, Mauritius

Printed at: see last page
ISBN: 978-620-0-52895-7

" IMAGES" IN ELECTRICITY

(Intellect and reality)

George Mpantes

Electricity denotes something imaginary, an entity which exists not actually but only in thought....Wiechert 1897

Can we express what we know about electricity in terms of something more fundamental? the answer is definitely no, we have only mental images!

Our acquaintance with it begins with charges and currents but we will never know it's real face, we will find it exerting forces, as molecules of a fluid (Coulomb), still in the field (Maxwell), in ether-light waves, in mathematical equations, intangible, hidden behind of mathematical concepts, an Aristotelian potentiality, still behind the description of space and time, in quantum fields (Feynman), is located at the crossroads of the great paths of physics, between quantum mechanics and relativity.

Written by George Mpantes

Mathematician

Serres Greece, September 2019

To my wife Marina

TABLE OF CONTENTS

Preface

We will soon see a small philosophical glossary that I believe is essential to understanding electrical theory and the concept of electricity.

Aristotle's holistic understanding of the human person is clearly represented in his understanding of the interactive relationships that exist between **senses**, **imagination**, and **thinking**. He believed that everything that exists in the intellect and the imagination must have first been in the senses.

Aristotle's model of psychology places great emphasis on the role that imagination plays in the dynamics of perception, thinking, and the subjective nature of experience. According to Aristotle, *"... imagination (phantasia) produces the **mental images** (phantasma) that play an essential role in the dynamics of the above-mentioned phenomena"*. Imagination, for Aristotle, is a necessary component of thinking in that it provides the raw content that is utilized in the processes of thought. Aristotle (on the soul),

> "...To the thinking soul, images serve as if they were contents of perception (and when it asserts or denies them to be good or bad it avoids or pursues them). That is why the soul never thinks without an image").

In other words, according to Aristotle, humans think in images. These images are object representations that are utilized in a variety of ways to provide the content for the various activities of the intellectual faculty (e.g., reasoning). The process of thinking involves the manipulation of these images or object representations. Furthermore, Aristotle thinks of images as being the very content matter of thought. He wrote:

> ...Since it seems that there is nothing outside and separate in existence from sensible spatial magnitudes, the objects of thought are in the sensible forms, viz. both the abstract objects and all the states and affections of sensible things. Hence no one can learn or understand anything in the absence of sense, and when the mind is actively aware of anything it is necessarily aware of it along with an image; for images are like sensuous contents except in that they contain no matter."

The unobservable reality

Operational definitionalism holds that meaning is constituted in empirical operations. Bridgman taught that the task of science was fundamentally empirical description. Aristotle retracted the claim that "a concept was synonymous with its corresponding set of operations". Rather, an operational definition was a necessary, but not sufficient, constituent for scientific meaning. Aristotle's view is that

> "..If there is nothing conceivable beyond phenomena (per se), but everything was sensible, we would have no science for anything except if one says that sense is science. Aristotle, *metaphysics 999b 1* »

Galileo, expressed in a famous passage of the Assayer (book in 1623) the conviction that perceptual features of the world are merely subjective, and are produced in the "anima"! the unobservable is a central topic in philosophy of science. The notion that a given unobservable exists, is referred to as **scientific realism**, in contrast to instrumentalism, the notion that unobservable such as atoms are useful models but don't necessarily exist.

From a purely philosophical view, the thought that the fundamental building blocks of nature are not immediately apparent to us, could be

[6]

regarded as primary. The great progress made by Greek philosophy was the recognition that any fundamental description of nature had to consider entities that were not readily available - our world is presented in an incredible variety of phenomena and materials, and their explanation must be inevitable. Some of the more fundamental (and obviously different) objects are beneath the world of surface features. There is no operational definition for them.

Are observable the *current element* of Ampere? No, because only closed circuits are accessible to experiment, but his law gave the right answer in all observable cases.

Are observable the Fechner particles? They are conceivable but they founded the Weber's force which gave the answer to all old theories of electricity (at-a-distance theories).

Is observable Maxwell's electromagnetic field? It is conceivable but it is the foundation the electromagnetic waves.

What are the geometric points? They are conceivable, without dimension, that is, not measurable, but they establish the straight geometric line.

Quarks do not exist as free individual objects! it seems that ordinary matter gains its mass from zero mass building blocks!"That is to say, this main characteristic of physic's matter, comes from mathematical truths, equations lost in the realm of meditation. Wheeler's ingenuity of "mass without mass" reminds us of geometry as "length without length" since the building block of length is the metaphysical point of zero length.

All of the above are unobservable as they are conceivable, and we attribute this distinction on more or less intuitive reference to the conclusions of accepted theories of the layman. Ultraviolet light, for example, is observable, while the absolute space and motions of molecules in kinetic theory will be classified as unobservable, we will see it in quarks , Duhem integrates them in metaphysics which explains, " *gives meaning in natural laws'*, d'Abro in theoretical hypothesis, and all because physical theory is adapted to the human nature which constructs it. The cognitive mechanism of man is twofold, the intellect and senses together. For Aristotle it depicts the dualism between matter and form, in this dual nature of realities. Our senses tell us about phenomena, but the scientific basis is formed in intellect.

In Maxwell's electromagnetic theory, all electric currents are closed. We know that if we connect two conductors with different potentials to one wire, then one current flows from one conductor to another until the two potentials are equalized. One such a current is called open current because the path it defines is not closed. The originality of Maxwell's theory is that the circuit, although open, is in fact closed by the generation of another kind of unobservable current flowing from the second conductor to the first through the surrounding ether. This etheric current, which Maxwell called the *displacement current*, is unobservable, mathematical, is supposed to produce the same magnetic phenomena as the ordinary current. Maxwell's laws secures the law of **conservation of charge.** It was the discovery of a new natural phenomenon, that the changing electric fields produce magnetic fields. Mathematically it entails adding an additional term to the equations which described the electromagnetic changes prior to the time of Maxwell. But in whatever way, Maxwell's theory aroused serious interest when Hertz, by direct experiment, confirmed one of its major consequences (the electromagnetic wave). That is some unobservable become real, **or we must treat them as real,** as Einstein said about the absolute space of Newton:

"..what is essential is merely that besides observable objects, another thing, which is not perceptible, must be looked upon as real, to enable acceleration or rotation to be looked upon as something real.."

"... quarks and gluons, or more precisely their fields, are mathematically complete and perfect objects. One can fully describe their properties, using only concepts without requiring samples or measurements, gluons are objects which obey the gluon *equations* ... "Wilczek

How can we classify these unobservable entities ontologically? A brief reference to the Aristotelian ontology, I believe, would be useful for a follow-up.

[8]

Aristotelian ontology

Aristotle introduces his notions of matter and form in the first book of his Physics, his work on natural science. What do we mean by the word 'reality'? It is the key concept of Aristotelian metaphysics through the distinction between the potentiality and the actuality, finally between matter and form, which today can be 'recognized' in the concepts of quantum mechanics and quantum fields.

Aristotle discovered the concept of potentiality by observing daily changes. The calm surface of a lake contains 'potentially' its wave disturbance brought by the wind. Its waves do exist but " potentially" they exist as a possibility of water among many others *forms*. This potentiality is "something", not nothing. It is not less real from actuality. It is real not with the reality of 'actual' but with the reality of 'potential'. The first is verified by the senses, the second is necessary to become apparent the first. What is happening as actual (form), was dynamic in matter and activated, (actualization) took form ! for example the green tomato has the potentiality to be a red tomato. Without the potentiality of matter, there is no reality captured by the senses, *the form*, that is everything that can be known about the substance — the shape, the weight, the structure, etc.

Every substance is in potency and act for various properties. Change occurs when potency is elevated to act — that is, when what something potentially is becomes what it actually is. In this way, Aristotle explained change in nature: change is elevation of potency to act. The matter (which is the subject that persists in change) remains while the form changes.

Building on this, Aristotle introduced as a solution the dual meaning of being, potential (matter) and actual (form), (*Physics 194b6*), a distinction that can be so strongly recognized today in modern physics. Aristotle's double being is a great conception that has never been deleted from the vocabulary of concepts, in all seasons.

[9]

We must accept that the intellect and the senses are one and the same thing in Aristotle's ontology.

where the senses cannot penetrate, the intellect enters into place.

Heisenberg defines Newtonian physics as the "ontology of materialism". On the contrary, the entities depicted in the formalism of quantum mechanics will be perceived in terms of the Aristotelian concept of 'potential'. There, the potentiality (potentia) is associated with change and indefinable matter (Aristotelian).

Heisenberg wrote in *"physics and philosophy"*

> One might perhaps call it an objective tendency or possibility, a "potentia" in the sense of Aristotelian philosophy. In fact, I believe that the language actually used by physicists when they speak about atomic events produces in their minds similar notions as the concept "potentia." So the physicists have gradually become accustomed to considering the electronic orbits, etc., not as reality but rather as a kind of "potentia." *(pp. 154-5 in the 2007 Harper Perennial Modern Classics edition) "..*

Experimental particle physics encountered the "potentiality" in virtual particles.

> "... In quantum field theory, 'potential' or virtual particle is a spontaneous variation of the quantum field. Real particles are stimuli of quantum fields, which last so long that they can be observed. The "potential" or virtual particles are short-lived entities that appear in our equations, but not in the experimental detectors. (Wilczeck) By providing energy we can amplify the spontaneous fluctuations above a threshold, essentially converting (previously) potential particles into real ones.... these potential particles are created and lost rapidly, without having to travel long distances, we do not see them in the usual sense, unless we provide the momentum and energy needed to create them. The potential particles need external help to gain existence. (Aristotelian actualization) However, they appear in

[10]

quantum mechanics equations, and accordingly affect the behaviour of observed particles... .. Wilczek "p.79»

"... In quantum field theory, there are many observable phenomena resulting from interactions involving virtual particles, and even classical forces - such as the electromagnetic interaction between two charges - can be interpreted as interchange of many virtual photons, but their real "reality" or existence, is a phenomenon of philosophy rather than of science. P.Davies »

How far is this description from Aristotle's potential reality?

We move on to quantum reality whose first approach was the Maxwell field:

"... The repulsion of two charges such as electrons can be calculated from the results of the transfer of virtual particles between them. Potential photons cannot travel more than the wavelength. We can identify the "potential photons" with the electrostatic field which decreases in the inverse square of the distance ($1/r^2$) while the actual photons represent the later reduced electromagnetic radiation ($1/r$) and thus travel long distances. The electrostatic field contains energy but does not flow away. Radiation transfers energy from the source ... (P.Davies) »

The unobservable reality, seems then familiar and friendly to us through the Aristotelian "potential" reality, a possibility studied by, the intellect and only the intellect, through mathematics, (mathematical models) The senses are experimenting with the actuality. Because : *no one can learn or understand anything in the absence of sense, and it seems that logic confirms the phenomena and phenomena the logic, Aristotle*

There are not experiments in potentiality, but only mental activities, viz mathematics. There is not here the operational meaning of concepts, as in actuality. For this book the Maxwell field is a potentiality, and electromagnetic forces the actuality of electromagnetism. The *standard model in physics* is studying fields but searching for particles. With fields the intellect interprets and predicts the behavior of the particles and forces in the laboratory (senses)

[11]

Operationalism

Is a positivist philosophical view that the meaning of scientific concepts is to be given in terms of the operations which govern the application of such concepts. *"we mean by any concept nothing more than a set of operations; the concept is synonymous with the corresponding set of operations" (Bridgman 1927,).*

The field does not exist for the physics of operationalism. Operationalists do not believe that the fields (in our case the Maxwell field) are actually self-explanatory, they are a mathematical definition, and the mathematics cannot decide whether electricity is discrete or continuous. It is rather a potentiality in Aristotle's ontology.

> ....we are convinced that purely mathematical reasoning never can yield physical results, that if anything physical comes out of mathematics it must have been put in another form. Our problem is to find out where the physics got into the general theory.. Bridgman

INTRODUCTION

In this book, through the history of the ideas of electrical theory, we will observe how natural philosophy became mathematical, *the* *mathematization of physics,* this rise of the mathematical approach to the natural world, which has been a necessary condition for its progress. Today we are far from our simplistic intuitive notions for particles, forces, mechanistic imagery, etc., and mathematics has contributed to this increasingly abstraction in physics evolution.

... .Electricity was first appeared in 600 BC. The term came from the classical Latin electrum, amber, from the Greek ἤλεκτρον (elektron), amber. Thales of Miletus discovered static electricity in 500 B.C. by rubbing fur on substances, such as amber. The Greeks noted that the charged amber buttons could attract light objects such as hair, as a kind of magnet, but opposed to some mineral, such as a mineral permanent magnets, without the need for friction. Electricity would remain more than a mental curiosity for many centuries, until 1600, when English scientist William Gilbert conducted a careful study of electricity and magnetism, distinguishing the static electricity produced by rubbing energy from magnetism.

Deep acquaintance with it begins with charges and currents but we will never know its real face, we will find it experting forces, as molecules of a fluid (Coulomb), still in the field (Maxwell), in light waves, in mathematical equations, intangible, hidden behind of mathematical concepts, still behind the description of space and time, in quantum fields (Feynmann), is located at the crossroads of the great paths of physics, between quantum mechanics and relativity.

What we know for sure today is that the concept of electric charge is described as a fundamental property of matter, such as the concept of mass. We cannot interpret why the elementary particles such as electrons and protons, carry an electric charge, as we ignore why they have mass. We describe it as that property of matter, whereby two charged particles or objects interact without physical contact. The charge is quantized. The smallest charge that has been experimentally isolated is the negative charge of the electron with a measure e = 1,602.10-19 Coulombs. Even with Volta's discovery of the electric element, a new manifestation of electricity was presented for study and experimentation in the form of curremts. Electric current, also known as electricity, is the movement in the same direction of tiny electrically charged particles, the electrons, in a closed circuit (closed circuit). In an open circuit there is no electric current.

But things were not simple!

A new radical idea began to emerge when physicists delved into electromagnetic phenomena with the works of Faraday and Maxwell. It was the idea that the fundamental entities of nature were not particles, individuals or a similar set of objects located in space. In contrast, the fundamental entities were non-locally located fields spreading throughout space and time. As such they had a more elusive and impersonal nature - one would call it ethereal - indeed these fields were not directly visible to us at all, but we knew them through their effects. We cannot experimentally identify an (EM) field but only observe its effects on the electrical charges that happened to be attached on matter.

So began a conceptual adventure in electricity, which divided physicists for a long time, into "fans" of intangible fields and them of particle descriptions.

Far action theories include the theories of Ampere, Gauss, Weber, Liènard, Ritz, Clausius and the so-called old theories. The reader must understand that the discoveries of the first half of the 19th century that began in France and were spread in Germany centered on Weber, Gauss and their students in Göttingen, were not a secondary course in physics. The central line of thought remained, for almost the entire 19th century, which Maxwell saw as his starting point, succeeding between 1864 and 1873 with a purely revolutionary thought experiment.

Contact theories include:

the theories of ether (Faraday, Maxwell, Lorentz) with the alternative theory of propagated potentials. One of the objectives of this presentation is to illustrate how Maxwell came to his mathematical constructs of the work done before him by Oersted , Ampère, Faraday, Gauss, and so on, into a concise and precise mathematical form. Maxwell's ideas and equations were expanded, modified, and made understandable by the efforts of Hertz, FitzGerald, Lodge, and Heaviside. The last three are being referred to as the "Maxwellians."

At the end of this controversy we came to know two electrical realities: the electrons and the electromagnetic waves, the second being the waves of the field electricity, had the properties of light, so they presupposed a carrier material, it is the famous ether, and indeed there was a final compromise between the two realities. This is the end of classical electromagnetism.

But in the aftermath of our history, the theory of relativity forces us to abandon the concept of ether and with it the mechanical interpretation of electromagnetic fields:

> "... From the time of Maxwell, Physical Reality has been considered to be represented by continuous fields, governed by some differential equations and without any mechanistic interpretation of Einstein ..."

Now the connection of material to intangible was the great oddity of electricity, an entity without mass, which is the most important reference point of our intuition and our mechanistic experience. But yet, space without ether is unthinkable; for in such space there not only would be

[15]

no propagation of light, but also no possibility of existence for standards of space and time (measuring-rods and clocks), nor therefore any space-time intervals in the physical sense.

Later the evolution of physics, forces us to accept another paradox reflected in electrical theory: light has two natures. Wave electrical theory of light is a good approach to how light is propagated, and its particle theory - the photon - describes how it interacts, that is, exchanges energy with something else. Now what do electromagnetic waves represent?

Today the central message of our most fundamental physical theory, namely quantum physics, is that everything is made of quantized fields. *And these quantum fields, themselves, are made up of particles. The electromagnetic field? Made of particles called photons.*

> .. quantum theory has led to the conclusion that any field theory is associated with elementary particles which define it. The physical properties of these particles are included in the equations of the field and is associated with them. Field interpretation describes only the probability distribution of associated particles. So photons are kind of particle representing the electromagnetic field. The Coulomb interaction between two electrons produced by "virtual" photons generated at the point of an electron, propagated at the speed of light absorbed at the point where is the second electron .... **Heisenberg**

Today we can think of matter as consisting of ripples of various kinds of fields, such as the rippling waves on the coast (P.Davies) , called "fermionic fields" that interact with other types of fields "bosonic fields", all fundamental particles are considered "excitations" of their respective fields. For example, there is an electron field, a muon field and a Higgs field. This is the " standard model in physics" (Salam, Weinberg, Hooft, Wilczek, Gross) whose last successful test was the observation of the Higg's boson in 2012 at CERN.

We will present here the "images" as Aristotle calls the ideas, - *the soul never thinks without an image in fantasy*- referring to electrical theory from Coulomb to Einstein, with no reference to the quantum description, that is to say classical and relativistic electromagnetism.

Part one:

the old theories of   point charges electricity and far actions, (Coulomb, Ampere, Weber), where Weber was the prophet of electrons.

Part two:

field electricity of polarized ether, (Faraday, Maxwell, Lorenz) and Maxwell the prophet o electromagnetic waves

Part three:

the relation of electricity and matter(Lorentz, Einstein), the hurricane of electron, the negative experiments

Part four: *electromagnetism and relativity, the immaterial field, the prophecy of space-time.*

where we will observe the cooperation of the *intellect with the senses* proving that the two factors are co-formers of a physical theory.

A feature of the book, not usually found in text books, is the inclusion of a large number of quotations from the pioneers of electromagnetic, giving also a little historical inside.

I am particularly grateful to my wife for great help in preparing the manuscript. Also many thanks to the library of physics department of Aristotelian University of Thessaloniki for the access in the world bibliography.

George Mpantes

PART ONE: THE ELECTRICITY OF POINT CHARGES, FAR ACTIONS

1.1 what is Coulomb's electricity?

..the English philosophers, and perhaps the greater part of foreigners too, have now generally adopted the theory of positive and negative electricity. According to this theory, all the operations of electricity depend upon one fluid *sui generis* extremely *subtile* and elastic, dispersed through the pores of all bodies; by which the particle of it are as strongly attracted, as they are repelled by one other...**Joseph Priestley** the history and present state of electricity with original experiments London 1767

A first presentation of the course of electrical theory is the physics of Charles Coulomb, a French military engineer in the later 1700s, who was the first that measured electricity. Here the imaginary idea , the image– that produces mathematical model- is that electricity is attributed to molecules of two kinds of fluid, a substance, as also for magnetism itself. These molecules exert forces with each other.

With his researches on electricity and magnetism, Coulomb brought this area of physics out of traditional natural philosophy and made it an exact science.

And in **physics of the laboratory** are the operations with a torsion balance, with one of the charged spheres on the arm of the balance, and the other held by a sliding wooden stick set over a scale. Coulomb verified experimentally the Priesley law (charge is the quantity of this fluid) that:

[18]

"The repulsive or pulling force between two small spheres charged with the same (or the opposite) kind of electricity is inversely proportional to the square of the distance of their centers, ... whatever the cause of electricity, we can explain all the phenomena on the assumption that there are two electric fluids that are repulsed or attracted to the other or the same fluid parts ....Coulomb"

But he did not find any connection between attraction and repulsing charges, he believed simply they were due to different types of fluids

The Coulomb force is $\rightarrow$

$$F_{12} = k \frac{q_1 q_2}{r^2} \quad (1)$$

Coulomb's apparatus today

with $F_{12} = -F_{21}$ after changing the orientation of r (Third Law of Newton) and confirming the attribute that emerges in phenomena, that in nature there are no forces, but only paired "interactions" that Newton has recognized since the 17th century. The ratio k is the electrostatic constant. In 1687, Newton showed that the gravitational attraction between two bodies also followed the so called inverse square law.

In relation to (1), magnetostatics is a force between two magnetic molecules, which developed greatly through the work of the great mathematician Simeon Dennis Poisson (1781-1840), who talked about the magnetic fluid and published in 1824 a mathematical treatise on magnetism analogous to this electrostatics, since the laws of electrical and magnetic power were in the same form as the force of gravity (central conservative power with special mathematical properties). In 1812, with a memoir at the French Academy - Poisson- accepted the hypothesis of two fluids and the expressions of the Coulomb.

[19]

"... when all parts of a body provide equal amounts of the two fluids, this body does not exert any force in the neighboring body fluids, so no electrical phenomena occur. A similar relationship was confirmed by Coulomb and the magnetic force confirming the descriptions of John Mitchel (1724-1793) where again appear the magnetic fluid and its molecules. This equal and even distribution of the two fluids is called a physical state, and when this condition is disrupted in a body, this body becomes electrified, and the various electrical phenomena begin to occur "(Poisson)

The comments on the nature of electricity begin just now! ...

...while admitting electricity as we have now done , to the rank of a physical quantity , we must not too hastily assume that it is or is not a substance; or that is or not a form of energy; the quantities "electricity" and "potential" when multiplied together produce the quantity "energy" it is impossible therefore that electricity and energy should be quantities of the same category...the use of the word "fluid" has been apt to deceive the vulgar, including many men of science who are not natural philosophers...for my own part, I look for additional light on the nature of electricity from a study of what takes place in the space intervening between the electrified bodies....
Maxwell

Here Maxwell prepares us for his own substance: the ether, but

"..in the scientific world the conception of substance is wholly lacking, and that which most nearly replaces it-viz. electric charge-is not exalted above the other quantities of physics. **Eddington"**

".. So we cannot seriously hold that q is a substance, then we must speak of measurement of electric substance. ..**Pohl** "

"...The measurements involved in these operations are measurements of ordinary mechanical forces...this of course is all very trite; The important thing for us is merely that magnitude of charge or quantity of electricity is an *independent physical concept* and that unique operations exist for determining this...the operations by which the inverse square law is established presuppose that the charge is given as an independent concept, since the operations involve a knowledge of charges....**Bridgman** (operationalism)

But what is the electric charge?

"...the special properties of the atomic fragments give rise to phenomena which we find it convenient to call electric phenomena...we can if we like call the atomic fragments themselves particles of positive or negative electricity as the case may be; or we may speak of them as particles charged with positive or negative electricity-that is a little more than a matter of taste. We know nothing of their ultimate constitution; and our ignorance in this respect is never likely to be dissipated-and i am afraid i can say no more in answer to the question, What is electricity? **L. Southerns**, electricity and the structure of Matter 1925 p.112"

So the first answer from the first measurement of electricity in physics is therefore: electricity means something whose presence is manifested in Coulomb's phenomenon. Or electricity is the measure of number q, through Coulomb's force. Whether entities which act thus are substantial , is a question for philosophers.

1.2 The forgotten theory of
Andre' Marie` Ampere

Here Coulomb's fluid molecules move, become electric currents, and exert forces with each other different from stationary charges. These also define magnetism, the magnets consist of currents. The ultimate hypothesis, the image, is the **current element**.

The story begins when the Danish Ørsted on 21 April 1820, during a lecture, noticed a <u>compass</u> needle deflected from magnetic north when an electric current from a battery was switched on and off, confirming a direct relationship between electricity and magnetism To the great surprise of Oersted and the students, the magnetic needle was no longer pointing to the north. This discovery was the beginning of a new chapter of electrical theory.

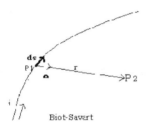

The first "interpretation" was by Jean-Baptiste Biot and Felix Savart who, on October 30, 1820, at a meeting of the Academy of Sciences announced that this force F exerted by a ds (very small) section of the conductor, flowing from current i, on a magnetic pole, that is to say, a point of space r (is a force between -current on magnet) and can be described in relation to these magnitudes (law of Biot-Savart is known in text books). It was a magnetic force (magnetic induction) generated by an electric current. The currents generated a magnetic field that changed the orientation of the magnetic needle. This relationship measured Oersted's phenomenon, but did not interpret it. The deeper phenomenon - the genius Ampere had first thought - was not the Biot-Savart magnetic force <u>but the force between currents</u>

"...... When Mr. Oesterd discovered the effect of a current on a magnet would be assuming the existence of a mutual action on two

[22]

circuits carrying current. However, this is not a necessary consequence. Because although an iron rod acts on the magnetic needle there is no mutual action between two iron bars ... Ampere.

Ampere discovered and calculated the forces between the currents, and then identified the magnets with the currents. Biot-Savart's force was interpreted as an electric force between currents, and magnetism became an effect of electric currents. He supposed that in the case of permanent magnets, the magnetism is caused by tiny electric currents moving in circles, which he referred to as the magnetic molecule. This connects the magnetic phenomena with the electric current through the *"principle of equivalence":*

"Any closed loop that is leaking by current is equivalent to a magnet."

principle of equivalence

Ampere's theory makes unnecessary the supposition of the existence of a magnetic entity, all magnetic phenomena being attributed to moving electric charges.

... there is no magnetism in this theory, and magnetic fields are supposed to be produced only by the movement of electricity ...
Wilson

.... we have nothing to do but to consider electricity as a primary concept and magnetism as a derived concept ...... **Planck**

... magnetism is seen in comparison to the reality of electrons and protons, as a fantasy that does not correspond to anything real ...
.**Guntherschule**

Indeed, we know that there are no magnetic charges in nature.

[23]

1.3 The hypotheses of Ampere

1. He assumed that the force between the conductors can be considered as a sum of forces between infinitesimal currents, the"**elementary currents**" as the infinitesimals of Leibniz. He "broke", that is, the current geometrically, into tiny and oriented elementary segments, ids, the "current elements". So the magnetic effect of a part of a circuit could be a simple sum of the individual interactions, which is common in Newtonian practice.

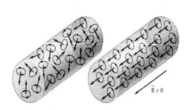

the bar magnet

2.Ampere not only accepted "electric molecules" but also envisaged an explanation of his formula : we must conclude that these phenomena are due to the fact that the two electric fluids continually traverse the conducting wires with a very rapid motion uniting and separating alternately in the intervals between the particles of the wires...when we suppose that(the electric molecules) set into motion in the conducting wires by the action of the battery, continually change their position...

3. assumed that the force between two elements of the circuit acts along the line joining them.

4. assumed that the force between circuits would meet Newton's third law, i.e. they would be equal and opposite, which is a mathematical affair and cannot be extracted from experiments

[24]

1.4 the experimental data of Ampere force (the laboratory)

• Two currents moving in parallel wires as parallel streams are attracted, while antiparallel being repelled. Still two elementary currents in the same straight moving uniformly tend to repulse each other, and moving counterparts are attracted (the *longitudinal forces*, forces in the direction of current)

• A small conductor, perpendicular to another, does not feel any force.

• The magnitude of the force is proportional to the product of the currents conveyed by the conductors.

• The magnitude of the force (force law) between parallel conductors is inversely proportional to the square of the distance, the force law of Ampere, $F = \dfrac{ii'dsds'}{r^2}$....

The experiments which Ampere carried out to test his hypothesis and to determine the laws of interaction of current-carrying wires, still valid today, were a model of simplicity. They involved the arrangement of wires, either straight, circular, or wound into spirals known as helices, in various geometric configurations one to another.

In order to verify his *force law* Ampere used a simple current balance (an apparatus used to measure the force between two current carrying wires) that consisted of two fixed, straight, vertical and parallel current carriers (wires) and a sensitive spring scale. He was able to adjust the distance between the wires and to measure the different currents through them with a simple compass galvanometer, and to measure the force exerted between the wires with his spring scale. Ampere used for his current measurements a magnetized moving needle or compass galvanometer.

Basically, the moving needle galvanometer Ampere used was a compass wrapped with a coil of wire. The stronger the current that passes through the wire, the greater the needle will be deflected. Or more correctly,

[25]

the tangent of the angle of deflection of the needle is proportional to the strength of the current in the coil and that's the reason that these meters are called *tangent galvanometers of Ampère's circuital law*

This picture is a modern model of the same device that Ampere built

for his famous experiments with which he connected magnetism to the electric currents

1.5 The mathematics of Ampere, circuital law

In the figure we see the elementary currents ids ids´ , coplanar, at a distance r where we analyzed their directions in two vertical components, (idsσυνθ, idsημθ) and (ids´ημθ´, ids´συνθ´). From the experimentally exported we have that the force between idsσυνθ ⇄ ids´ημθ´ as between idsημθ ⇄ ids´συνθ´ is zero (perpendicular currents). Therefore, the action of the two elementary currents ids and ids' goes back to the action of pairs idsημθ ⇄ids´ημθ´ as of idsσυνθ ⇄ ids´συνθ´ where one pair are parallel forces and the other pair longitudinal (they act in the same line r) so from experimental data we have

$$dF = \frac{ii'dsds'}{r^2}(\eta\mu\theta\eta\mu\theta' + k\sigma\upsilon\nu\theta\sigma\upsilon\nu\theta').$$

[26]

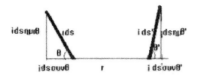

the mathematics of circuital law
of Ampere

When we want to calculate the force that one circuit exerts on the other, we need a double line integral. The difficulty of mathematical operations does not prevent conclusions that are consistent with experimental results. A valuable partner of Ampere in the extraction of his conclusions was Felix Savary.

"... it is reasonable to assume that without the help of **Savary**, Ampere would never have the time to complete the detailed calculations required, in the application of the type of force he produced, to the magnetic phenomena ..."

The formula certainly represents the macroscopic results, provided the currents are steady and uniform and at least one of the circuits is closed. But it

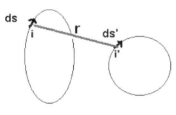

the circuital law in imagination

leaves quite open the question of the physical significance of "current elements" and does not decide whether the force is directly exerted between the linear conductors or only indirectly through the currents.

But according to Maxwell

"this formula must always remain the cardinal formula of electrodynamics"

However, the removal from the Newtonian school first appeared, since the force between the elementary currents was not described by a simple law of inverse squares but also by their angular position. This was the reason why Ampere's work had been ignored for about a decade.

[27]

With this *magical formula* as Maxwell wrote, one can comprehend all phenomena even if the elementary currents have a questionable physical existence.. It is the first hint of atomism in electricity.

Interactions of elementary currents are not directly observable, since elementary currents cannot be isolated in the physical state. What is experimentally verified is the force between closed currents resulting from the integration of forces (Ampere or Grassman) along the closed currents (closed curve), verifying the original Ampere case.

1.6 Critique of the ideas of Ampere

The law of Ampere describes a far action like the Coulomb law.. He defends the formula has produced, avoiding to be placed in the subject of contact action, or action at-a-distance.

"... Whatever the natural cause of this action, - the power between currents - the formula i have extracted will remain the expression of the facts. If we succeed to explain it from other assumptions - such as contact action or the oscillations of a fluid that extends into space - we shall have advanced a further step in this branch of physics But this inquiry, with which, while appreciating its importance i have not occupied myself ,will not change the results of my work, since to be in accord with the facts, the hypothesis adopted must agree with the formula which represents them so completely ..., **Ampere**"

...The experimental investigation by which Ampère established the law of the mechanical action between electric currents is one of the most brilliant achievements in science. The whole, theory and experiment, seems as if it had leaped, full grown and full armed, from the brain of the 'Newton of electricity.' It is perfect in form, and unassailable in accuracy, and it is summed up in a formula from which all the phenomena may be deduced, and which must always remain the cardinal formula of electro-dynamics. **Maxwell, A Treatise on Electricity and Magnetism 1873, 2 p.175"**

Later on with the atomic view of electricity, the physical cause of this action was revealed: charged particles.

"... we must consider the Ampere types to be primarily dependent on the interactions of the electrical particles of the current and only indirectly manifest themselves as actions on the conduits ... .Weber"

The effort of physicists to interpret Ampere force and elementary currents beyond mathematical results is depicted in the following passages:

"... The type of Ampere has only historical interest (!) ... Bouasse"

".. The analysis of elementary currents is only ideal ... Hertz" [1]

"The method of the element of a circuit is a purely fictitious one, since an element of a circuit cannot exist alone ... Starling"

".. Strictly speaking from the Maxwellian point of view, there is no such thing as mutual action between elementary currents. This action is indeterminate, so we have a large number of so-called theories of electrodynamics... Heaviside[2]"

Obviously he refers to "old theories".

"... The mutual actions of a closed uniform current and a magnet, the actions of a magnet on a segment , great or small of a current are quantities that really exist. They can be observed and measured. But the action of a elementary current with a magnet cannot be observed. Such action has no real existence. It is a mathematical

---

[1] If there is nothing conceivable beyond the senses there is no science for any thing ... ..Aristotle, the theoretical hypothesis

[2] But there are forces between currents. Real for Heaviside is Maxwell's field. Today we accept Ampere's idea of magnetism as due to micro-currents as an account for the relevant phenomena. Heaviside's controversy with "continental science" as he calls it, will culminate in his critique of Weber's theory.

fiction which serves an intermediary for calculating the action of a closed uniform current on a magnet....Duhem[3]

The idea of reality of elementary currents, apart from the mathematical arrangement of force between the currents, reduced the acceptance of the Ampere forces from the scientific community, till the emergence of atomism of electricity, where, Ampere's elementary currents acquired a physical basis.

Ampere, like Maxwell, is abstained from an idea of atomism of electricity. He, however, makes mathematical atomism. Maxwell rejects it by calling a "coarse affair." Ampere imagines the currents as Leibniz imagined the curve as a set of infinite infinitesimals, a model manageable of integration and infinite calculus. But such subtractive images also exist in Maxwell's electric theory:

"... in theory of Maxwell, the 'quantity of electricity" is just an abbreviation of the integral $\iint D dS$, ...it is not a physical quantity or at least need not be so ... ..Shafer »

Here we have the Maxwell electricity as an incomprehensible fluid which fills all space. Mathematician Ampere attributed mathematical atomism to electricity. Mathematician Maxwell used other mathematics to delete it's atomism !

Is the Ampere force an outdated force? Theoretically, the compatibility of this force with Maxwell's theory is still a matter of discussion. Today the "Ampere memorandum" is almost never mentioned. Only a small section of its two hundred pages has been translated into English, even in France have difficulty working with the Ampere law. The reason is that fifty years later, Maxwell gave a new mathematical formalism to the laws of electricity, that as he claimed, is equivalent to the formalism of Ampere and his successor, Weber.

---

[3] This for Duhem is the "explanatory component" of a physical theory it is a metaphysical hypothesis – our imagine agent- and will be judged by the results of the experiment.

Thus today, a completely different picture appears in the University textbooks. We have a course through the concept of field, the Ampere force "is described through field", the same as the course of Coulomb's force in stationary charges through the law of Gauss. Ampere's force became the force of Biot-Savart to describe the magnetic field that has now becomes a reality, but the animated idea is the basic principle of **Ampere's equivalence,** which was also "translated" into the field language as *Ampere circuital law* in integral form:

$$\oint B dl = I$$

which later expressed in differential form, as partial differential equations involving the divergence and curl operators (Maxwell equations).

1.7 Faraday's philosophy, the induction

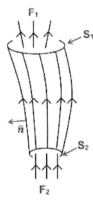

a tube of lines of force

Faraday's experimental work in electromagnetics led him to accept that electric and magnetic force are not directed at a distance, but are carried by a physical medium possessing mechanical properties. He usually described the electric and magnetic effects using the concept of *"lines of force"*. The image is that electromagnetic forces are carried by lines of force stretched between electric charges. . The electrostatic induction is ascribed to "inductive lines of force" not to a direct action at a distance . This effect seemed to propagate from point to point through the medium.

[31]

....I do not perceive in any part of space, whether vacant or filled with matter, anything but forces and the lines in which they are exerted. Space must be a conductor , or else the metals could not conduct...I feel great difficulty in the conception of atoms of matter...with intervening space not occupied by atoms...[on this view] matter is everywhere present.. matter will be continuous throughout (Faraday experimental Researches in electricity 1849)

This is the dominant idea of Faraday in its 'favourite' and most complete form:

that the **various motions of the lines of force in the continuous substance which fills all the space**, exert the forces through the substance. These features of Faraday's 'favourite notion' were carried on. Maxwell, in his approach to the problem of finding a mathematical representation for the continuous transmission of electric and magnetic forces, considered these to be states of stress and strain in a mechanical *ether* (the substance) exerted through the *electric displacement*.

The idea of these force-lines, probably first made familiar by the conformation of iron particles round a magnet, became so real to Faraday that he indulged in the speculation that light and radiant heat were tremors of the lines of force...the ether , which in another view is supposed to be the medium in which this vibrations take place.

Yet he believed in "the possible and probably physical existence of lines of force for gravitation, electrostatic, magnetism,. The great propagandist of this view has been Sir J.J.Thomson, who tells us as late as 1925 *"that these lines are not merely geometrical figments but that they-or rather the groups of them forming tubes of force, that end on an electron-are physical realities.....The conception of lines of force is in my opinion one of the greatest of Faraday's many great services to Science ....J.J.Thomson"*

...These ideas , though long ignored , was ultimately received with an enthusiasm which persists even today. "nothing has proved of greater importance and more fruitful than this conception of lines of force, which is "a fundamental advance for all time" **Lenard**

[32]

But what about of the old electrical theory?

According to the older mathematical theory of electromagnetism (mainly due to Ampere) the existence of a magnetic field is inseparably connected with the motion of charged bodies or at least charges. There is nothing in theory to suggest that there could be a magnetic field apart from the motion of charges. But according to Faraday the magnetic field is associated, not with the motion of charges, but with the motion of the tubes attached to them; and since the tubes are flexible there is very reason to suppose that the tubes might move without the charges,,,,**N Campbell**)

But are all these a reality image?

…this is certainly a good example of the self-hallucination induced by one's own vocabulary. We obtain the expression of the force vector at any point. We then draw the tangent-lines of this vector as a useful graph. To strengthen our belief we call them "tubes", now we endow them with "flexibility" and declare that they "might move without the charges" from which we started. Then we pick out one portion of the force on moving charges and call it "magnetic force" and similarly attribute to it flexible independently moving tubes' Finally , we declare that this double system of tubes is "the only important theory which has ever been proposed to explain "electricity, magnetism and light. This tube-theory is a most ingenious specimen of soporific phraseology **Alfred O'Rahily p.650)**

However the contemporary use of lines of force is not equivalent to Faraday's concept, because we do not conceive of those lines as substantial physical realities "*Any explanation of this kind which attributes mechanical properties to lines of force is highly artificial as there no evidence for their existence. Nowadays physicists are becoming more and more inclined to shun such explanations; so the mechanical explanation of the interaction of electrically charged bodies is rapidly falling into disuse. It still lingers in text-books , however, and it is important to recognize its arbitrariness….J.Piley Electricity Oxford 1933 p.94*"

But all this philosophical physics justify the Prof. Soddy's complaint:

…At the present time , when so much of our theory is merely a transitional patchwork of new ideas upon old habits of though, rather than any consistent substitute for the old way of regarding thinks, surely all these old ideas ought to be critically examined, and, in accordance with the modern tenets, nothing allowed to be assumed which is not directly amenable to observation…mere familiarity and reiteration of ideas is taking the place of genuine theoretical advance amenable to scientific proof… F.Soddy," the interpretation of atom 1932. p. 341"

1.8 The phenomenon of induction

Creation electricity from magnetism

Formally, time independent electrical and magnetic properties can be described by considering electricity and magnetism as largely separate phenomena. However, when time dependence becomes part of the "equation" we find that electrical and magnetic properties become inextricably linked - electromagnetism.

Magnetism in some way generates currents, in the opposite direction to the Oersted experiment. This is a new phenomenon based on observation only.

Faraday will present a new way to produce abundant electricity through processes that will not be electro-chemical, - but electromagnetic processes. In the new phenomenon he will give the name *electromagnetic induction*. For the measurement of the generated current, it uses the concept of the *electromotive force* - which is not force but energy, it expresses the charge per unit of energy with which the circuit is fed due to the presence of the source. The electromotive force does not refer to two points - such as the potential difference - but to the whole circuit. Its units of measurement are the same as those of the potential. This action, through the potential difference, will feed the generation of electricity, we will refer to it as "electric energy"

[34]

In 1831, seven years after the Ampere investigations, the discovery of the phenomenon of electromagnetic induction introduced new data into the study of electric theory. A description of the whole phenomenon is the following:

Static electricity had the force of induction, that is to cause an

opposite charge on the bodies near it. Was it possible that electrical currents would behave like this? The idea was, in principle, that a current, was adjacent to another that was flowing from a current would also be leaking from an induced current that would last for as long as the induction. But that was not the case. A current was actually induced, but it only lasted for a moment, that the original current began to flow or cease. The induced current was not dependent on the mere existence of the inducing, but on the change of it.

But the Farady worked with magnets, coils, and lines of force.

The change could be produced by changing the magnetic field strength, moving a magnet toward or away from the coil, moving the coil into or out of the magnetic field, rotating the coil relative to the magnet, etc. by introducing the concept of **magnetic flux,** but without a mathematical description (Faraday was not a mathematician), but descriptively. This flow through the surface enclosed by the conductor, produces the induced current in the conductor!

"... If the circuit moves vertically or obliquely along the magnetic dynamic lines in one direction or the other, it eventually sums up the amount of forces represented by the lines with which it is crossed so that the amount of electricity (EMF) that entered the circuit (induced current) is proportional to the number of these lines ... Faraday »

Magnetic flux Φ and EMF are the two agents that produce the phenomenon of induction but in a descriptive way.

[35]

The two cases (the magnet approaching the circuit or inversely, had different and unexplainable significance in the Faraday era. When the circuit is

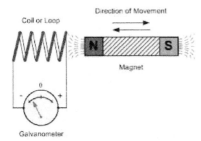

stationary, the force that drives the loads cannot be magnetic, since in stationary charges there are no magnetic forces. So what is the driving force in this case? Definitely an electric field. However, this will not be electrostatic since the electrostatic fields do not produce electromotive force (EMF). Obviously, therefore, this electric field that drives charges in the induced circuit, is induced by a changing magnetic field (Griffiths p.21)

In doing so, Faraday attributed a natural existence to the idea of magnetic lines of force. With lines of force we can get information not only about the direction of the magnetic force but also about its magnitude. The intensity of the field was characterized by the density of the dynamic lines of force per surface unit (flow), perpendicular to its address.

An evaluation of the role of lines of force in the change of physics (field theories) starts with Faraday who sometimes discusses them as having an existence all their own, this role begins to be deleted before its mathematical completion. Now give us a descriptive interpretation of current induction.

> "... .If the circuit moves perpendicularly or laterally along the magnetic dynamic lines, in one direction or the other, it finally sums up the sum of the forces represented by the lines intersecting so that the amount of electricity (emf) that went into the circuit (induced current) is proportional to the number of these lines ... Faraday »

The induced current in the circuit s depends on the time change of Φ, i.e. the number (flow) of the magnetic dynamic lines through the surface S enclosed by s (diaphragm) irrespective of the cause of this change. In the field language the change of a magnetic field generates an electric field.

[36]

The relationship is $\quad emf = -\frac{d\Phi}{dt}$

where the minus sign express the law of Lenz

While Faraday's law tells us the magnitude of the emf produced, Lenz's law tells us the direction that current will flow. It states that

"The induced current will appear in such a direction that it opposes the change that produced it."

In Maxwell we have*"A magnetic field changing with time induces an electric field"*

1.9 Neumann and Ampere

The term potential energy was introduced by the 19th-century Scottish engineer and physicist William Rankine, although it has links to Greek philosopher Aristotle's concept of potentiality. Neumann was the first[1] to write down the magnetic vector potential in his 1845 paper "General laws of induced electrical currents. The energy

Neumann (1845) proved that the system of the two closed currents of Ampere,

A. is a conservative system (that is, the Ampere force satisfies

F=-∂U/∂r),

And B. The laws of induction can be deduced from the Ampere analysis.

In fact, he succeeded in defining a U function in which if we apply -∂U/∂r, we have the Ampere force, that is, the U function is the Ampere potential, the dynamic energy of the elementary current system, and the Ampere force is a conservative force. The Neumann dynamic function for the elementary currents ids and i′ds′ when integrated along the circuits gives us the dynamic energy U of the current system (the energy stored in this system) with the relations

[37]

$$U = -i\int_s \vec{A}\,d\vec{s}......with.....\vec{A} = i'\int_{s'} \frac{d\vec{s}'}{r}.$$

That is, the dynamic energy of the two-circuit system equals its product i on the "circulation" of vector A along the closed curve s´. This dynamic energy generates the Ampere forces between the circuits.

Thus the potentials of the electric forces are known to us, φ for the static fields and the vector potential $\vec{A}$ for the currents.

The vector $\vec{A} = \int \frac{id\vec{s}}{r}$ is the Neumann vector potential of an elementary ids where we consider ds as a vector and r is the distance from where we want to calculate the vector potential. The vector expression of Ampere's force in Neumann's analysis stems from the fact that the force depends on the orientation of the elemental currents, while the Coulomb force depends only on the distance. Of course we cannot identify **A** with a measurable amount nor with a historical experiment, it is the mathematical description, *the potential reality of the phenomenon.*

1.10 Neumann and the induction of Faraday.

"Neumann's theory was a mathematical interpretation of Faraday's theory through the concept of its vector potential $\vec{A}$. He also discovered that the electric forces that produced the induced current were the rate of change of his (vector) potential from one current to another. He announced his results in 1845 and Boltzmann characterized them as the "mathematical phenomenology" of induction. Neumann's type of dynamic is still found in modern electrodynamics books and his style of mathematical physics has initiated a strong tradition in his country (Olivier Darrigol). "

[38]

Now Neumann will speak in the plain language of Faraday, interpreting the Ampere force as a Biot-Savart force, that is, the B-force of the magnetic field generated by the currents, in the language of mathematical electricity. *His interpretation is that the temporal variation of the magnetic flux in the receiver circuit (which flow is related to the elemental currents of Ampere (from the equivalence principle), that is, to the Neumann potential, is attributed to the time variation of the vector potential $\vec{A}$*. This idea stems from the intermediate relationship

$$\text{EMF} = - \int_s \vec{A} \, ds$$

However, the change of this flow Φ produces the induced current.

Thus, vector potential **A** will be linked to Faraday's theory of current induction, and this is the essence of Neumann's discovery, which in this potential corresponded to Faraday's dynamic lines.

"... by interpreting the magnetic flux $\Phi = \iint B \, ds$ in terms of dynamic lines, we see that the dynamic energy U represents the product of the intensity i, on the number of dynamic magnetic lines due to s′ passing through the surface surrounding circuit s. And since according to Faraday's law, the currents induced in s depend entirely on the number of these lines, it is obvious that the dynamic function U, that is, the potential A, supplies us with what is necessary for the detailed trading of the induction of currents. This was the discovery of Neumann .... Whittaker. "

For our presentation this means Faraday-Lenz's law

EMF$=-d\Phi/dt$, becomes   EMF$= \frac{d}{dt} \int_s$ **A**ds.   (Newman interpretation)

Finally, the concept of the vector potential of Neumann, links the two phenomena of electricity, the forces of Ampere and induction, in a single *'energy interpretation'*:

The slope of the Neumann dynamic energy raises mechanical forces between the fixed circuits $(F = -\partial U/\partial r)$. However, its temporal variation raises an **EMF**. Changes in A may be due to changing currents or changing the

[39]

position of the circuits. The speed of these changes is what determines the **EMF.**

Thus, every appearance of mechanical force on the circuits is always accompanied by electric force, since the former is determined by changes in current and position, and the second by the speed of such changes.

1.11 Weber's electric force, a fascinating electrodynamics

Weber's electric force gives directly the force between two charges that are in relative motion (charge - charge) , and not through the action of

omnipresent Maxwell's electromagnetic field (charge - field - charge) , the first is the action at a distance as Newtonian gravitational force, the second, *the hypothesis that attributes electric action to tensions and pressures in all-pervaring medium, being identical with that in which light is supposed to be propageted,* **Maxwell,** the interaction by contact through a medium , an old ideology-image, in physical theory .

W. Weber

The "old electrical theory" of Coulomb, Ampere, Neumann, Fechner, Weber, Gauss, Riemann, etc. was the mainstream of physics until the mid 19th century, and interpreted all known electrical phenomena. However, it has been deported from physics, after the victory on a fierce ideological fight, of the theory of the electromagnetic field of Maxwell, the British electrical theory.

For many independent researchers, this shift to the mathematical theory of Maxwell, is due to the eternal rivalry of the British school with the "continental science " that has existed since the time of Newton and Leibniz, the Bernoulli and Taylor, between British and ' non- British ' mathematicians and physicists. The rivalry imposed one electrical theory, and the other was forgotten[4]. The old theory was treated as a " sect[5] " that have to be expelled from the new British religion of field .

But we must not forget the strong point of field electricity: the electromagnetic waves .

Yet classical (the old) electrodynamics preceded the mathematical theory of Maxwell to all the great moments of physics. First it equated magnets with currents making magnetism electrical phenomenon (Ampere), developed electrostatics, interpreted the induction phenomenon, foresaw the atomism in electricity (that field electricity rejected) and founded the first electron theory. Still, the old theory gave the fundamental law of electrical force between moving charges (Weber), a new force in nature that depends on the relative velocity of the interacting charges, something completely new in physics, a law other than the induction and the Coulomb and Ampere forces, interpreted even the stability of the atom Bohr without quantum conditions, which in essence is the cancel (rather than generalization) of Maxwell's electrodynamics in the individual area of "very small". Even the old electrodynamics determined the radius of the electron, long before this was discovered, and made nuclear forces generalized forces of classical electrodynamics. Also many conclusions of relativity could be made from the

---

[4] Anything related to the electrodynamics of Weber, has to be written in textbooks since 1940.

[5] The theory of Weber was characterized as "heretical" by Helmholtz (Philosophical Magazine 44, 530-537 (1872)

old electrodynamics without the adventure of experiments for the determination of the ether, which certainly abolish the Maxwell field from the category of *natural concepts.*

The leader of the heretical electrodynamics, the man who described the electric force between moving charges without the mediation of the electromagnetic field, analogous to the Coulomb force for immovable charges, is the German Wilhelm Weber6

.....He (Hertz) spoke of the difficulty he had in getting his ideas accepted in Germany, where the professors were working under the theory of Weber, Neumann and others and did not understand Maxwell. The discovery of the electron has since that time recalled attention to these old theories, and rather justified their discontinuous treatment as opposed to the continuity of Maxwell. This is a subject with which, the scientific historian will have to deal; but time is not ripe for its discussion....**Hertz in a conversation with Oliver Load** [7]

...If anyone right price for the synthetic idea which unifies the various branches of electrical and magnetic science that is Weber . Today, those who still support the ether theory or profess the relativists, accept those principles that were introduced or developed by him: that Ampere's idea (the magnetism is due to micro - currents) can explain all related phenomena. That electricity has atomic structure, that currents are streams of electrified particles, that Ampere forces act directly between these particles and not between the pipes, that Coulomb's law should be modified for charges in motion, that the electrical action is not instantaneous (Gauss), that the laws of

---

[6] Weber was born in Wittenberg in 1804 where he took his first lessons from his father. He studied physics in Halle . His performance was high, and after he took his doctorate in 1822, he was appointed as associate professor in University of Halle.

[7] Advancing science , 1931, p.110

electrodynamics and induction should be drawn from statistical aggregation in a law that connects charged particles ..... **A Rahily**

«..Weber's electrodynamics was the first electron theory...»[8]
Whittaker

1.12 The electric force of Weber

The discoveries of Ampere were noticed from Gauss, in University of Gottingen. The studies on magnetism and electricity had cemented his belief that the top problem in science was to confirm the laws of Ampere. Seeking help in his investigations, he proposed cooperation in a young physicist Wilhelm Weber. Together they designed a new device, the *electrodynamometer* , which fully confirmed the conclusions of Ampere, as they explored the possibility of a new electric force in nature.

The results of a rigorous program of instrument building and experimentation, interrupted by Weber's expulsion from Göttingen University as a result of the political events of 1837, as he fought for his constitutional rights against the king of Hannover (1830), and were finally published at Leipzig in 1846.

These results completely confirmed the deductions of Ampère, andalso introduced a new physical principle.

The persistence of Gauss was directed on the idea that two elements of electricity in relative motion, repel or attract each other in a different way, when they are in relative motion or at rest. That was his bet in electrodynamics

The ideas of Gauss developed there after Weber who continues in Leipzig the confirmation of Ampere's experiments and communicates with Gauss.

---

[8] In an electron theory, all electrical phenomena relate to interactions between moving charges or not, that the forces between them depend not only by the distance but also from their speed.

[43]

The target now of Weber, was an interpretation of the law of Ampere so that except the reduction of magnetism in electrical phenomenon, still electrostatic to be connected with the electrodynamics (be part of) and moreover to interpret the phenomena of induction which were interpreted by the Faraday 's hypothesis of field . Then we would have a complete theory of all known electrical phenomena without the assumption of the field, but with the discovery of electric force at a distance between stationary or moving (relatively) charges. Beware: the <u>relative motion</u> that involves in Weber electrodynamics , is crucial to relativity , but also to the study of atomic phenomena . Two charges moving with equal speed and parallel to a reference system are in *relative rest* , and to Weber's electrodynamics the force between them is the Coulomb force. Unlike the Lorentz force formula, use's a speed relative to a medium!.

Weber considered together with Fechner, (Fechner hypothesis [9]) the presence in a conductor, positively and negatively charged particles. The voltage in the conductor, actuate these particles, with equal but opposite velocities. So, if we consider the *elementary current* of Ampere as a minimal portion of the conductor containing each time a positively and a negatively charged particle moving in opposite directions, then between two elementary currents, there are four interactions must be taken into account, in Ampere's interaction . With the law of Coulomb, these four actions which are two attractions and two repulsion cancel each other . But Ampere showed that between the current carrying conductors, forces are exerted, so there is a hidden force that is not described in the law of Coulomb. This hidden force that might be interpreted beyond the action of Ampere, the Coulomb force and

---

[9] Fechner assumed that the electric current consists of a flow of electrical charges of two types of positive and negative. For every positive charge there is a corresponding negative that is equal in size to the positive, but moving in the opposite direction with this.

induction (Faraday).The interaction between these two elementary currents essentially refers to four interactions between charged particles, (figure 2.1)

1. between +e and -e'
2. between +e and -e'
3. between -e and -e'
4. between -e and +e'

And as the particles are limited on the conductor, we assume that the forces between them, carry the motion in the conductors themselves. .

force between two charges in motion

which he presented in his influential 1846 paper "Electrodynamic Measures on a General Fundamental Law of the Electric Action". The law was fundamental in the sense that the electric action applied to electric "masses" themselves rather than to their ponderable carriers, the conducting wires

1. the longitudinal motion

Weber first considers the case where two elementary charges move along the same line, and determines the forces specified by Ampere as longitudinal forces(Figure4.1) If the two elementary currents of each case were at rest, the two attractions of opposite charges 2 and 4 would equate the two opposing repulsion of particles 1 and 3 . We would have therefore dynamic equilibrium. But from the experiments of Ampere, we know that there is longitudinal repulsion in motion in the same direction (left figure)and attraction   in   opposite   (right   in   figure)
The question is: *how to modify the electrostatic Coulomb's law, that have the result of longitudinal forces ?*

[45]

The idea is the following: when the elementary charges are at rest the system of four charges equilibrates. When moving the same direction, they

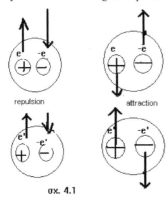

repulsion   attraction

σx. 4.1

repel each other. So the attractive force of equilibrium decreases (while moving in opposite direction decreases the repulsive force of equilibrium), but we must understand that the reduced action is the action of the charges with relative motion, because the attraction is produced from the opposite charges moving with relative motion , the homonyms move in the same direction with the same speed. (in contrast, the repulsion decrease from the relative motion of homonymous charges).

So

Finally in the motion of repulsion (same direction), the opposite charges have relative motion so the attraction (produced by opposite charges) decreases and appears repulsion. In the motion of attraction (opposite direction), the homonyms charges have relative motion, so decreases the repulsion and attraction occurs. From this interpretation Weber formulated the theorem that: the electrostatic force should be reduced when electrified particles are in relative motion, that is when they have relative speed .

Coulomb 's Law is ee'/r^2 and the relative velocity of two bodies denoted $\dot{r}$. Since Weber 's theorem applies to the removal and approaching of particles - that is, when the signs of the relative velocity is positive or negative - Weber will use the square of the relative velocity , and since the electrostatic action is reduced by the relative speed of electrified particle, he expresses his theorem for the force between two particles in longitudinal movement

where a is a constant to be determined .

[46]

$$F = \frac{ee'}{r^2}(1 - \alpha^2 \, \dot{r}^2) \ldots\ldots (2.1)$$

2. The parallel motion .

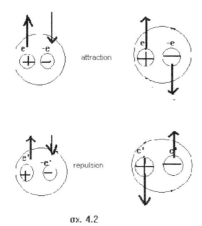

σx. 4.2

The same considerations should now be applied in the case of two parallel elementary currents that form a right angle with the line which connects the middle of them . (Fig. 4.2) In this case the effect (attraction or repulsion depending on whether the currents flow to the same or the opposite direction) was known to Ampere from his first experiments . The interaction will be discussed now, as in the previous case, consistent with the hypothesis Fechner.

In the case of attraction which cancels the known electrostatic equilibrium as the electrodynamics interaction depends on the relative velocity of the particles, the result is that is not the repulsion that decreases, as homonyms charges have no relative velocity. So what happens is that actually the attraction increases. How do we interpret this ?

At the time that the elementary currents are exactly opposite to one another, the relative speed of the oppositely electrified particles is zero so the effect of the attraction is not interpreted with the presence of the relative speed. But before this coincidence, the particles have negative relative speed (the distance diminishes) and after that it grows (positive relative velocity) In the point of meeting the relative velocity changes sign from negative to positive. This change of relative velocity is *the relative acceleration.* So the moment we study (the elementary currents are exactly opposite one another), the charged particles have relative acceleration but not relative speed. It is this relative acceleration that produces the additional attraction between opposites, and

[47]

additional repulsion between the homonymous. Namely, while the relative velocity decreases the electrostatic action, now the relative acceleration increases.

So Weber added a term to the previous expression of force and the ultimate resulting force is

$$F = \frac{ee'}{r^2}(1 - \alpha^2 \dot{r}^2 + \beta \ddot{r})........2.2$$

where the term $\ddot{r}$ symbolizes the relative acceleration.

generalmotion

The last operation in the formula is to consider the case that the elementary currents do not move in parallel conductors, but their relative position is determined by a function r = r (t). then the result   (Weber 1846 , par.19 becomes

$$\ddot{r} = \frac{1}{r}\dot{r}^2 \quad F = \frac{ee'}{r^2}(1 - \alpha^2 \dot{r}^2 + \frac{\beta}{r}\dot{r}^2 ....2.3$$

the coefficients

To establish a relationship between the coefficients α and β Weber returns once again in Ampere's work and especially in the point that was mentioned in a letter to Gauss on March 19. The ratio of the coefficients in equation 2.3 is nothing but the ratio of forces between parallel elementary currents and longitudinal elementary currents that Ampere was estimated to have an absolute value ½. Thus Weber sets

$$\alpha^2 = \frac{1}{2}\frac{\beta}{r} \implies \beta = 2\alpha^2 r$$

And the general expression for the force between two electrified particles becomes

$$F = \frac{ee'}{r^2}[1 - \alpha^2 \dot{r}^2 + 2\alpha^2 r \ddot{r}]......(2.4)$$

Considering the four intermediate relations that exist between each pair of particles in elementary currents,   Weber divides the constant a with 4

[48]

deducing in the 1846 work, the force between charged particles , where he applies this power to the phenomenon of induction

What remained was to determine the value of the constant α.

In 1855 Weber and Kohlrausch conducted experiments[10] which determined with great accuracy the value of constant denoted by α. They found that $4 / α = 4.395 \times 1011 = \sqrt{2}c$ ...... (2.5)

(c the speed of light, which was then known as the ratio electromagnetic to the electrostatic unit of charge[11]) , and this value with the symbol c_w became known as Weber 's constant . He described the c_w, as the relative speed that should hold two electrical masses, so that there is no interaction between them.

If we set $c_w = \sqrt{2}c$ then the final form of the Weber force which is the *fundamental law of electrodynamics* is

$$F = \frac{ee'}{r^2}[1 - \frac{1}{2c^2}\dot{r}^2 + \frac{r}{c^2}\ddot{r}]......(2.6)$$

where c is the speed of light.[12]

The Weber force law all particles, regardless of size and mass, will exactly follow Newton's third law. Therefore, Weber electrodynamics, unlike Maxwell electrodynamics, has conservation of particle momentum and conservation of particle angular momentum.

---

[10] Riemann who participated in the experiment, soon expressed hiw belief for the deep relationship between light and electrodynamics

[11] Maxwell measured this constant in 1868 but has entered this in his displacement current in 1861, borrowed from the electrodynamics of Weber ... AkT Assis

[12] Wilhelm Weber, "Elektrodynamische Maasbestimmungen: über ein allgemeines Grundgesetz der elektrischen Wirkung," Werke (Berlin: Julius Springer, 1893) Bd. 3, pp. 25-214. English translation in 21st Century Science archive (Determinations of Electrodynamic Measure: Concerning a Fundamental General Law of Electrical Action)

1.13 Weber's potential

The Weber force depends on the relative speed and relative acceleration of the bodies. Such a force appears for the first time in physics, and so there have been unprecedented controversies among the great physicists of Europe.

For now Weber has to prove that his force behaves like the other known forces, e.g., gravity, Ampere, that is, the work produced by it in any process can not be unlimited, that is, energy cannot be produced from zero. In other words, the new force should derived from a potential, which in the German-speaking world was widely accepted and used. (F. Neumann, Clausius, Weber, Kirchoff, Riemann).

In Britain the situation was different. Despite the significant contribution of Green, Stokes, etc. to the theory of potential (the term potential, due to Green), they insisted on separating kinetics from dynamic energy, considering the kinetic energy as essential.[13]

In the context of the German tradition, Weber has shown that his power comes from a speed-dependent potential, opening up a great debate (a strong confrontation with Helmholtz) on the conservation of the energy of his force.

He considers the function

$$U = \frac{ee'}{r}(1 - \frac{\dot{r}^2}{2c^2})$$

from which he will produce his force:

$$-\frac{1}{\dot{r}}\frac{dU}{dt} = \frac{-1}{\dot{r}}(\frac{\partial U}{\partial r}\frac{dr}{dt} + \frac{\partial U}{\partial \dot{r}}\frac{d\dot{r}}{dt}) = -\frac{1}{\dot{r}}\{-\frac{ee'}{r^2}(1 - \frac{\dot{r}^2}{2c^2})\dot{r} - \frac{ee'}{r}\frac{\dot{r}}{c^2}\ddot{r}\} =$$

$$\frac{ee'}{r^2}(1 - \frac{\dot{r}^2}{2c^2} + \frac{r\ddot{r}}{c^2}) = F_{Weber}$$

---

[13] JJ Thomson attempted to show this supposed priority, and Maxwell described the idea of *"retarded potentials"* as "inconceivable"

that is, Weber's force is a conservative force.[14]

It is shown by the formula of potential energy U, that if the relative velocities of the particles to one another become constant equal with c_w, then the electrical force between them becomes zero. So he reaches the notion of **the limiting speed of light** for material bodies, 35 years before the theory of relativity by a completely different course from that of Einstein.

In terms of this sense of potential and the energy interpretation by Neumann of Ampere law, Weber interpreted the Ampere force from the charged particles of electricity he introduced. He demonstrated the energy equivalence of his law with that of Ampere and produced the Ampere law from his speed-dependent potential. .
(P. Graneau)

1.14 The Weber law in the Interpretation of Induction

The law of Faraday's induction can be derived from Weber's electrodynamics as identified by Maxwell himself in the Treatise (article 856).

"After deducing from Ampere's formula for the action between the elements of currents, his own formula for the action between moving electric particles, Weber proceeded to apply his formula to the explanation of the production of electric currents by

---

[14]In 1851 Helmholtz traveled all over Germany and met the most outstanding physicists. In a letter he observes that Weber welcomed him *"with far less cordiality than his brother in Leipzig"*. For many, the relationship between the two men was influenced by the profound rivalry of their ideas, namely the criticism of Helmholtz in the discoveries of Weber. Thomas Hirst describes Weber as follows: *"He speaks and stalls incessantly, you only have to listen. He often laughs without any obvious reason and you regret you cannot communicate with him. "*

[51]

magneto-electric induction. In this he was eminently successful, and we shall indicate the method by which the laws of induced currents may be deduced from Weber's formula....Maxwell [15]"

Indeed, the Weber force is associated with the vectorial **Neumann potential** and through it with the theory of induction, but in a completely different basis, without the concept of lines of force. Fechner charges crossing the induction circuit at the same time, vary (by virtue of Weber's force) differently the kinetic state of the particles of the second circuit, resulting in the induction currents.

Whittaker writes:

"The necessity of induction currents can be deduced as a general conclusion from the basic assumptions of Weber's theory. When a circuit **s** moves into a field due to currents, the velocity of the positive charges in **s** is not equal to and opposite to the velocity of negative charges. This fact produces a difference in the forces acting on the positive and negative charges in **s**. From this fact, the opposite charges are separated and move in opposite directions. "[16]

---

11. A detailed proof of this fact can be found in : Derivation of Faraday's law from Weber's force. A K T Assis, Weber's electrodynamics (Kluwer Academic Publishers, Dordrecht, 1994) ISBN: 0-7923-31

[16] "A history of the theories of ether and electricity Whittaker

1.15 The debate with Helmholtz, the principle of conservation of energy

The successes of the new force met the recognition and skepticism of top European theorists, starring Weber and the German School on the one hand, and Helmholtz and the British School on the other.

The controversy in the field of electrodynamics arose from the fact that the two Maxwell-Weber theories are mathematically equivalent but conceptually incompatible and on the other hand there are experimental difficulties with open circuits for an experimental confrontation, so the investigation accepting one or the other, turned to various unifying principles of physics, such as the principle of conservation of energy.

Following the controversy with Weber in the field of energy, Helmholtz in 1886 introduced a new unification program in physics based not on energy conservation but at the principle of least action. The principle of energy conservation is abandoned as the main driver of physics since it 'applies in a wide variety of cases where least action is not valid. So the latter is more special. "

Weber presented his force law in 1846. Only one year after this Helmholtz published his famous and influential work dealing with the **conservation of energy**. His main result is that forces depending on velocity and acceleration, or which act in other directions than the lines which unite each two separate material points, for example, rotatory forces, then combinations of such bodies would be possible in which forces might be either lost or gained ad infinitum, so are in contradiction with the conservation of force or energy.

Based on this statement, Maxwell and others thought that Weber's electrodynamics did not comply with the principle of conservation of energy (after all, although Weber's expression is a central force, it depends on the velocity of the charges). (AKT Assis)

Maxwell only changed his points of view in 1871, **after Weber's proof of the law of potential.** There is a reproduction of a post card from Maxwell to Tait, dated 1871, in which Maxwell informs Tait that Weber was right when stating that his (Weber's) electrodynamics did comply with the principle of conservation of energy. In this post card he says:

'Weber is right, his force has a potential which involves the square of the relative velocity. Hence in any cyclic operation no motion is spent or gained.' Helmholtz's proof cannot be applied to Weber's force because this expression depends not only on the distance and velocity of the charges but also on their accelerations. And this more general case had not been considered by Helmholtz".

And finally Maxwell admitted in hos Treatise(484) that the objection from the conservation of energy "does not implay to the formula of Weber.

However, in British electrical literature, Helmholtz's position that the Weber power did not meet the principle of energy conservation was acceptable for twenty years. Maxwell accepted it in 1865, Thomson in 1867, Tait in 1868. The change was made with Maxwell in 1873 only after Helmholtz himself retreated.

But Helmholtz's critique continues. It **is the second phase of the confrontation.**

Weber's potential is not always a positive quantity! Its electromotive part can be infinite by diverting the entire potential to unlimited negative values. Then the system will produce an unlimited amount of work.

"... the charge behaves as if it were of negative mass, so in some cases its velocity can be increased indefinitely under the action of a force opposing in motion ..." Helmholtz "

Maxwell agrees with Helmholtz and claims:

"... this impossible conclusion is a necessary consequence of accepting any type of potential that introduces negative conditions to the coefficients of the v^2 ..."

But Zoellner seems to understand the deeper meaning of confrontation

[54]

"... I have never met such a plethora of absolute nonsense in a small space of thirty lines .. Zoellner"

Weber notes that there should be a limit speed for bodies in nature, which will prevent this development. It is easy to see that the Weber potential becomes negative when $u_r > c\sqrt{2}$. Therefore, this velocity according to the Weber case is limiting for the electrified particles. This velocity is the constant of Weber's equations. Helmholtz's criticism, therefore, had to be rejected because it provided a relative particle velocity greater than $c\sqrt{2}$. By limiting this speed, its potential is always positive. But what is that speed? Its natural meaning of the Weber constant c is that if the relative particle velocity becomes constantly equal to c_w then the electrical force between them is zeroed. Thus, Weber reaches the concept of the marginal speed of light for material bodies 35 years before the theory of relativity through a completely different course of Einstein's course.

"...In the present state of science this is completely unjustified because it is impossible to verify the case of the two electric fluids. And moreover, because the conclusions are incompatible with the principle of conservation of energy, for which we have many experimental results to perceive it as a general principle of nature. These theories are particularly dangerous when it comes to interpreting more phenomena, such as the induction currents interpreted by Weber.. **Thomson and Tait on treatise on natural philosophy..**"

It seems that the climate of confrontation was quite warm in the second half of the 19th century. Other German physicists were involved in this debate. Carl Neuman entered in 1875 on Weber's side, Rudolf Clausius in 1875 on the other side.

"... opposing theories of electricity - the theories of Faraday Maxwell's medium and the theories of Gauss, Weber, and Riemann's of distance action - are in the field of intense confrontation. The theories of natural phenomena based on the assumption of distance action can only be temporary, and must necessarily be replaced by the theories of the medium, as science develops ... Sir O. Lodge (1881)

But what is the underlying cause of confrontation?

It was none other than the Newtonian doctrine of contact action that dominated the English School of Theoretical Physics.

"... The dogma of action from a distance, developed to a great extent by the French and German sciences, and formed the basis of Weber for an almost complete electrical theory. The distance action was challenged by Newton himself and was therefore not adopted by the English School of Physical Theory ... Livens'

Contact action was definitely an image of our everyday experience in electrical theory. The action from a distance stimulates the human mind. But it has often appeared in physics that the human mind is often overlooked by nature.

"... With the term distance action, Schuster writes, we realize that two bodies can interact with one another without being connected to each other by some means that conveys the power. To me, it seems that a dogmatic denial of remote action is the survival of an ancient anthropomorphic interpretation of natural phenomena ....Schuster: the progress of physics during 33 years , Cambridge 1911".

Really understanding the ability for gravity to be an inherent property of matter or Coulomb's inherent charity property requires a distraction from the world of everyday experience that supplies us with images of contact action. How would we treat as an entity the electric charge and the force it exerts?

Epilogue for far actions

The doctrine of action at-a-distance...was specially favored by the French and German scientific schools, and in W. Weber's hands is an almost complete electric theory was built upon it. The doctrine was, however, strongly repudiated by Newton himself, and hardly affected the English school of

[56]

theoretical physics. But we must call our attention to the great and wonderful simplification which electrical theory has undergone in the course of this school.

Although it has been demonstrated that, in certain aspects, the Weber force formula is consistent with Lorentz force, they are not exactly equivalent—and more specifically, they make various contradictory predictions as is described in the APPENDIX. Therefore, **they cannot both be correct.**

Eventually in these few lines, we see that the history of electricity is always seasonable, since it seems that the electric force connects round it directly or indirectly, all the concepts of modern physics.

this investigation is discussed in the following texts

Assis, AKT; HT Silva (September 2000).

"Comparison between Weber's electrodynamics and classical electrodynamics". Pramana. 55 (3): 393

Assis, AKT; JJ Caluzi (1991).

"A limitation of Weber's law". Physics Letters A. 160 (1): 25–30.

Junginger, JE; ZD Popovic (2004).

"An experimental investigation of the influence of an electrostatic potential on electron mass as predicted by Weber's force law"

Wesley, JP (1990)

"Weber electrodynamics, part I. general theory, steady current effects". Foundations of Physics Letters. 3 (5): 443–469.

PART TWO: THE FIELD ELECTROMAGNETISM

A conceptual difficulty in Newtonian mechanics, however, is the way in which the gravitational force between two massive objects acts, over a distance across empty space, or in electromagnetism how an electric force operates between two charged particles. Newton did not address this question, but many of his contemporaries hypothesized that the forces were mediated through an invisible and frictionless medium which Aristotle had called **the ether.** The problem is that everyday experience of natural phenomena shows mechanical things to be moved by forces which make contact. Any cause and effect without a discernible contact, or action at a distance, contradicts common sense and has been an unacceptable notion since antiquity. Whenever the nature of the transmission of certain actions and effects over a distance was not yet understood, the ether was resorted to as a conceptual solution of the transmitting medium. By necessity, any description of how the ether functioned remained vague, but its existence was required by common sense and thus not questioned.

2.1 Faraday's image: the lines of force

The origin of Maxwell's field are the *Faraday's lines of force*. These lines are used to explain the action of forces from a distance. Faraday, the great experimenter philosopher, was the first to conceive the concept of the electromagnetic field. He distinguished, a reality of another class from that of matter (electrotonic state), it was something real that was taking place in electric and magnetic phenomena. It was capable of carrying influences from place to place without being treated like a mathematical structure as the gravitational field of its time. In his opinion, the phenomena of electricity and magnetism should be accessed through the field rather than through the charged bodies and currents. In other words, according to Faraday, when a current flows through a conductor, the most important aspect of this phenomenon was not the electric current, but the fields of electric and magnetic forces distributed to the round from the area of the current.

> For Faraday the magnet was no an ordinary lump of matther but a metal –bellied super octopus stretching multitudinous, invisible tentacles in all directions to the uttermost ends of the world.It was by means of such tentacles –magnetic tubes of force- that the magnet was able to pull the iron to itself… (Banesh Hoffman)

In 1835 for wrote for intermediate particles that their contact transfers electrical activity:

> .... It seems probable and possible that the magnetic action can be transmitted at a distance, through the action of intermediate particles in a way that similarly the forces of static electricity are transferred in distance. Interfering particles, we assume for the moment, that they are in a special situation that I often express
>
> (without much success) by the **term electrotonic state….Faraday**

This Faraday's view became conviction for many generations of physicists, after the domination of mechanical models in electricity.

[59]

Physicists were used to illustrate the magnetic forces, scattering iron filings on a piece of paper and observing the lines formed by the action of a magnet underneath the paper .. These lines submitted to Faraday the idea of magnetic lines of force with which , he claimed, we can get informations not only on the direction of the magnetic force but also on its size. The intensity of the field, characterized by the density of field lines per unit area , vertical in it's direction. .. *I do not perceive in any part of space whether (to use the common phrase) vacant or filled with matter can help myself, anything but forces and the lines in which they are exerted ...***Faraday***[17]*

Later in the study of dielectric media he introduced electric field and *electric lines of force*, wherein the reduction or the increase of the density of these lines was describing the behavior of dielectric.

For example how work the lines of force in the law of Coulomb;

In Faraday's view, the medium intervenes between the electrified spheres - whatever it is - manifests attractions and tensions The field lines piercing the lower half of the sphere transmit a tension that is parallel to the field. This is a stress pulling downward on the charge from below. The field lines draped over the top of the imaginary sphere transmit a pressure perpendicular to themselves. This is a stress pushing down on the charge from above. The total effect of these stresses is a net downward force on the charge.

The lines of force exert mechanical actions! The idea of this spreading action from point to point through a medium with the effect of adjacent and contiguous particles, were applicable to every area of physics in Faraday's theory.

He believed in "possible and probable physical existence of lines of force for gravitation, electrostatics, magnetism"

---

[17] "Experimental researches in electricity"

[60]

There are the lines of gravitation force, those of electrostatic induction, those of magnetic action in any part of space in which they are exerted...**Faraday**[18]

He indulged in the speculation that light and radiant heat were tremors of the lines of force:

" a notion which, as far as it is admitted, will dispense with the ether , which in another view is supposed to be the medium in which these vibrations take place" ....**Faraday**

Thus, the lines of force become an independent reality, they are the " the nervous system" of the medium, which moved charged and magnetized bodies.

"...Instead of an inviolable action at a distance between two electrified bodies, the Faraday considered the entire space between the bodies taut and full of mutual driven off loops ..... The concept of dynamic lines are in my opinion one of the biggest services Faradayto science ...

J.J.Thomson

"..... The view consolidated views of Faraday delivers a real existence in the dynamic lines in the sense that they exist as an independententity...**Grimsehl-Tomaschek**

...." As a result of the researches of Faraday and Maxwell we regard the properties of charged bodies as due to lines of force which spread out from the bodies into the surrounding medium" ... **E.W. Barnes**, Scientific theory and religion)

It is better to imagine (to understand Faraday) that these ' energy pathways ' did not appear there simultaneously with the iron filings, but there exist like landscape around the magnet, and now the iron filings are drifted in their topography. This image, intuitively touch better in our imagination-phantasma- than the idea that around the magnet there is nothing and that all

_____

[18] "Experimental resrescarches in electicity"

phenomenon is created by placing the iron filings. This is the reason why the medium theories eventually passed through the consciousness of physicists.

But what are their springs? How they can transfer energy? In Faraday's field, where mathematics is missing, physical processes become Aristotelian qualitative descriptions :

> "....According to Ampere the existence of a magnetic field is inseparably connected with the motion of charged bodies. But according to Faraday the magnetic field is associate, not with the motion of charges, but with the motion of the tubes (of lines of force) attached to them; and since the tubes are flexible, there is every reason to suppose that the tubes might move without the charges....**N.Campbell, modern electricity theory Bambridge"**

They are qualitative descriptions as Albert O'Rahily says[19]:

> ...we obtain the expression of the force -vector at any point. We then draw the tangent-lines of this vector as a useful graph. To strengthen our belief we call them "tubes" . Next we endow them with "flexibility" and declare that they "might move without the charges" from which we started. Then we pick out one portion of the force on moving charges and call it "magnetic force" and similarly attribute to it flexible independently moving tubes. Finally we declare that this double system of tubes is "the only important theory which has ever been proposed to explain electricity magnetism and light......**Alfred O' Rahily**

Today we know that the lines of force are not   so a service to science, as a contribution to the educational process. The natural assumption which underscores (the ether) has been removed. The situation described in the following passage, brings us back to the operationalism   in definition of concepts in physics.

> ...any explanation of this kind which attributes mechanical properties to tubes of force is highly artificial as there is no evidence

---

[19] Electromagnetic theory by Alfred O' Rahily Dover

for their existence. Nowadays physicists are becoming more and more inclined to shun such explanations; so the mechanical explanation of the interaction of electrically charged bodies is rapidly falling into disuse. It still lingers in text-books, however, and it is important to recognise its arbitrariness…**Piley** [20]

Faraday, being purely experimental with little knowledge of theory, could not perceive an electric field with the purely mathematical way. So he introduced the lines of force and he believed in their material substance. .

Maxwell continued and described mathematically exactly the ideas of Faraday's lines of force, the field that intervenes in electrical phenomena . The electrotonic state became **field** and was installed as an absolute (materials in genesis) reality.

…We are unable to conceive of propagation in time, except either as the flight of a material substance through space or as the propagation of a condition of motion or stress in a medium already existing in space …**Maxwell**[21]

This is the famous new reality of electric field:

..in theories of action by contact, the intensity of the field is a reality that exists even though the reactive charges are removed ......
P.Hertz

.... The theory of Maxwell continues to yields a shelf existent reality to the vector E independent of the presence of the test (second) charge ...... **Abraham-Becker**

The space in and around a given system of charges is called the electric field of those charges... **Livens**

The space within which these Faraday tensions manifest themselves is called the field …**Schaefer**

---

[20] Electricity Oxford 1933
[21] Treatise…p.492

2.2 The school of Cambridge, the genesis of field

In prevalence of theories of electric medium which began with the intuitive interpretations of Faraday, the main protagonists apart from him, was the whole "school of Cambridge" of natural philosophers (as Tait , W.Thomson, Heavyside, etc himself Maxwell) founded by Green, Stokes and W. Thomson, which (school) was dominated by the belief that all physical action is founded on dynamics.

> ....I am never satisfied if i can not construct a mechanical model of something. Then only i can understand. And this is why i could not capture the electromagnetic theory ...... I had not a moment of peace or happiness in relation to electromagnetic theory from November 1846 ... **W. Thomson**

His objection was a natural one. It was one thing to think of a displacement current in a dielectric filled with atoms. It was quite another to imagine it forming in the nothingness of a vacuum. Without a mechanical model to describe this environment and without actual moving electric charges, it wasn't clear what displacement current was or how it might arise. This lack of a physical mechanism was distasteful to many physicists in the Victorian era.

[64]

Thomson, began to investigate the proportions of electrical phenomena and flexibility. These surveys showed a picture of the spread of electrical and magnetic activity. He made the suggestion that they spread like the spreading the elastic displacement in an elastic solid. He was unable to promote his instructions connecting the ideas of Faraday to the mathematical proportions had invented. So towards the end of his life in 1896 after the failure of login electromagnetism with mechanical models wrote:

....A single word characterizes my efforts on scientific research over the past fifty years. I do not know anything more about the electric and magnetic force, the relationship of the ether of electricity and matter than i knew and i taught my students fifty years ago ....**W Thomson**..

1861. Fields and charges are initially conceived as mechanical states in Maxwell's theory, but without a detailed description. In 1861 Maxwell publishes a mechanical model of the electromagnetic field**, "on physical lines of force**" and this mechanical model played a crucial heuristic role in the evolution of his electromagnetic theory. Thomson's analogies between electrical phenomena and elasticity, helped to inspire James Clark Maxwell established a mechanical model of a magneto-electric medium and compared the Faraday's lines of forces with the lines of flux of a fluid. Maxwell's magneto-electric medium is a cellular ether, looks like a honeycomb. Each cell of the ether consists of a molecular vortex surrounded by a layer of idle-wheel particles, and the electromagnetic field becomes a factory of the industrial revolution in Britain. But the relationships that govern the operation of this field are Maxwell's well-known equations.

1864 In his 1864 lecture, and the paper that followed,-*a dynamical theory of the electromagnetic field,* he left the mechanical model behind but kept the concept of displacement current. Focusing on the mathematics, he described how electricity and magnetism are linked and how, once properly generated, they move in concert to make an electromagnetic wave.

> ...It happens a tulle of phenomena in electricity and magnetism lead to the same conclusion as that of Optics, namely that there is an ethereal medium that permeates all bodies and is differentiated only by their presence. That the parts of this medium are tucked in motion by electric currents and magnets, that this movement can spread from one part of the medium to another through forces generated from the connections of these parts, that the influence of these forces generated deformation dependent upon the elasticity of these connections, and finally as a consequence of all this, it is possible to show the energy of this medium in two forms, one as kinetic energy of the parts and the other as dynamic energy of its connections as a result of their elasticity ...**Maxwell**

So then we see that we are leading to the assumption of a complex structure capable of a multitude of movements, but also having such connections, that the movement of one region depends according to specific relations with the movement of other parts, which moves associated with forces that are born from the movement of the joined elements thanks to their elasticity. Such a mechanism should be the object of the general laws of dynamics.

Maxwell's first step was to translate the seemingly mystical ideas of Faraday into the more familiar language of mathematics of Cambridge school. From these labors was born an important new physical concept, the field, which was later to form the basis of Einstein's general theory of relativity.

So there are two tendencies in Maxwell's work: the first is the attempt to explain electrical actions by the properties of the hypothetical medium which is their carrier and the second is a purely mathematical description by means of partial differential equations based on the assumption of certain vectors specifying the electric and magnetic state of a body. Electricity

[66]

accordingly exists in two entirely different forms: **the electric substance within the conductor and the electric field in free space.**

1873. He publishes "*Treatise on electricity and magnetism*", which presents everything that was known in his time about electromagnetism, through Faraday's ideas.

...The electric field is the portion of space in the neighbourhood of electric bodies, considered with reference to electrical phenomena... Maxwell

..The space all around a magnet pervaded by the magnetic forces is termed the field of that magnet.....Livens

..The space within which the ether is sensibly disturbed and within which sensible ponderomotive forces are exercised ..is called the electrostatic field....Drude

...There is said to be an "electric field" in a region which is traversed by lines of force...Bragg

..In the near action theory the field strength is a reality which exists even when the reacting bodies are removed ... Hertz

...E is not the actual strength of the electric field at the point where the charge e is situated, but rather the field-strength that would exist at that point if the charge e were not present at all...Planck

...We must suppose that it E exists at all points about q even when our test charge is not present; but we can prove it's existence only by bringing the test charge to q...White

.... The idea of Faraday's force field -the field- has fundamentally changed our picture of the world ... B. Bavik

Maxwell continued and described mathematically exactly the ideas of Faraday's lines of force, the field that intervenes in electrical phenomena and was installed as an absolute (material in genesis) reality. The essence of the above field approaches in Faraday's perception is the assumption that when there is not   second charge, the lines of force exist and *move towards infinity*. But without the second charge they are nonexistent. The flow of Gauss in the Coulomb field is fantastic, it is a mathematical trick to

[67]

simplify the results. But in Faraday's scope becomes real, is the material factor that produces the phenomena. How real are all these?

> ...Any statement which is made about the electric field in the neighbourhood of a charged body cannot strictly speaking be taken to mean more than that a second charged body, if placed there, would behave in a particular way...the physical reality of the magnetic pole remains as questionable as that of the electric field ..**J. Piley**

> Even more decisively Leech, carries us back to pre- Faraday period.

> ..... The electric field variables φ and E are not subject to direct observation but their values can be derived from observations in material systems. A clear understanding of this fact could prevent questions about the nature of these variables. Their reality should be attributed as follows: to be considered as mathematical entities whose importance lies in the possibility to use them to describe and predict observable changes in the behaviour of exclusively material systems ..... **Leech**

Mathematical entities...but the mathematical entities became basic concepts of real word.

> ....it follows that the (Maxwell's) equations form a consistent scheme, independently of the hypothesis from which they have been derived,...independently of any physical interpretations which may be assigned to the various terms of the equations....we may if we please to discard Maxwell's interpretation. **James Jean**

Here Bridgman says:

> ...there would seem to be no necessary inherent in the requirements of the model itself, that all the mathematical operations should correspond to recognizable processes in the physical system. Nor is there any more any reason why all the symbols appearing in the fundamental mathematical equations should have their physical counterpart, nor why purely auxiliary mathematical quantities should

not be invented to facilitate the mathematical manipulations, if that proves possible…**Bridgman**

Well, what is going on? May be the charge produces a change in the state of the surrounding ether, may be the charge extend into the region about it, or is something incapable of description in mechanical terms. But the important point is that if another charge is placed at any point of such space it will be acted on by a force and accelerated. The issue touches on philosophy. In operationalism view this important point is the only point.

> …I believe that a critical examination will show that the ascription of physical reality to the electric field is entirely without justification. I cannot find a single physical phenomenon or a single physical operation by which evidence of the existence of the field may be obtained independently of the operations which entered into the definition ….i do not believe that the additional implication of physical reality has justified itself by bringing to light a single positive result, or can offer more than the pragmatic plea of having stimulated a large number of experiments, all with persistently negative results…..the electromagnetic field is an invention and is never subject to direct observation. What we observe are material bodies with or without charges-including eventually in this category electrons- their positions, motions and the forces to which they are subject. **Bridgman**

2.3   The electric displacement

> … Maxwell teaches that the movements of electricity are like those of an incompressible fluid so that the total quantity of electricity within a closed surface, always remains the same. It shows that what he meant by electricity was something different from a collection of electric charges …… **J.J.Thomson** '

[69]

Maxwell introduces the new image of electricity in Article 60 "in *Treatise on electricity and magnetism*", through a conceivable experiment between imagination and mathematics.

"...We imagine a charge q uniformly distributed over a spherical surface (Σ) so that the intensity E at a point P that is a

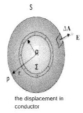

the displacement in
conductor

distance r from the center, is q/r^2, according to the Coulomb law.

this intensity according to our theory is accompanied by a displacement of electricity (flow) in a direction towards the outside of the sphere. ..The displacement, this flow, outward of a spherical surface concentric to Σ is equal to the charge enclosed in the sphere. So we have led to a remarkable conclusion of our theory that the electrical movements are similar to those of an incompressible fluid, Maxwell "

This is the metaphor of the *electric displacement*. It is as a displacement of an uncompressible fluid.

...Maxwell treats electricity as an incompressible fluid which fills all space...Clausius.

In field images we have the innovation that $q = \iiint \rho dV$ the point charge becomes a distribution in volume.

What is this?

Now we are no longer talking about point charges but for a finite density ρ in space so that the infinitesimal charge $\Delta e = \rho \Delta \tau$ is contained in a $\Delta \tau$ volume element, which tends to zero ...

As for the current, this is the movement of the previous volume.

[70]

The electric displacement is Maxwell's most central hypothesis on electricity, as Euclid's 5th axiom for geometry, we are to say the "ladder" by which he reached its mathematical prophecy of the existence of electromagnetic waves. ***The analogy, he says, between the action of electromotive intensity in producing electric displacement, and the ordinary mechanical force in producing the displacement for an elastic body is obvious.***

When a molecule of this electric fluid is disturbed from its position of normal equilibrium, Maxwell says that there is electric "displacement" (electric flux) produced by E, i.e. q, as the earthquake generates a tsunami. He shows that the quantity M of this electric displacement passing through any closed surface Σ or S in the shape, is constant and equal to q. How is this flow measured? In mathematics is measured by a new vector, the vector of the electric flux density M, called electric displacement and denoted D. It is defined by Maxwell as follows:

D=E in empty space and D=εE, ε the constant of the medium. We have the sequence q$\rightarrow$ E$\rightarrow$M =D

"... Whatever electricity is, and whatever we mean as a movement of electricity, the phenomenon we called "electric displacement" is a movement of electricity just as electricity movement is the transfer of electricity through a wire. ... ..Maxwell »

But:

"The amount of displacement is measured by the amount of electricity passing through the unit of the surface, the changes in electrical displacement obviously constitute electric currents ....
Maxwell"

Now here we have the leading image of this phenomenological theoretical study, where Maxwell modeled the treating of electricity:

"We have very little experimental data linking the direct electromagnetic effect of currents with the change in electrical displacement in dielectrics, but the extraordinary difficulty of

[71]

reconciling the laws of electromagnetism with the presence of closed currents is one of the many reasons why to accept the existence of inductive currents due to displacement changes. Their importance will be seen in the electromagnetic theory of light ... Maxwell »

The hypothesis of electric displacement is the substratum of the ultimate revolutionary concept of Maxwell's electricity, that of the *displacement current.*

2.4 The displacement current

The idea is this:

Here Maxwell considers as a current something which is not a flux of electricity. This is the basis of the theory in 1864.

Next to Article 60, Maxwell introduces his major theoretical hypothesis that we will briefly describe

"... when an electromotive force acts on a conductor, it produces a current through the conductor. But if the medium is dielectric, the current cannot continue to flow in the medium, but the electricity within the dielectric is displaced in the direction of the electric voltage. Changes in electric displacement obviously constitute electrical current ... **Maxwell »**

$j = \partial D/\partial t$ (is the electricity flow) which equals the conduction current i since q = M. So **the circuit is not interrupted**, which for Maxwell was a mathematical requirement. That means that no displacement takes place except on the condition that the circuit remains closed.

What happens in the dielectric? this arrangement in the shape of dielectric molecules, is a bridge for the passage of electricity, something like electric current!

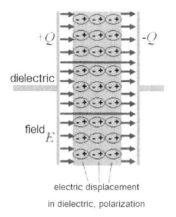

electric displacement
in dielectric, polarization

The same happens, but vice versa when the capacitor is discharged. **But this process is not only for dielectric but also for empty space and this is the great idea**! Ether for Maxwell was "*a pervading medium with small but real density*" When such a medium is subset to electric stress it might behave as an ordinary dielectric was believed to behave.

Dielectrics or insulators are called materials such as oil, glass, grease, etc., which do not allow electric charges to move inside them. We know that in an electrically neutral atom, the center of positive charges and the center of negative charges are identical. When this atom is found in an electric field, then these centers are shifted between them so that they are no longer identified. The atom ceases to be electrically neutral and corresponds to an electric dipole, the phenomenon is called **polarization**. Here we have another fluid. Maxwell supposes that the matter of dielectrics is filled by a hypothetical *elastic fluid* analogous to the aether which in optics is supposed to fill transparent bodies;

he calls it elastic electricity. *So in Maxwell's language , the electricity of dielectrics is supported to be elastic, while that of conductors is supposed to be inert (Poincare ́)*". We have here two different properties assigned to two fluids called by the same name-electricity. According Faraday displacement was applicable only to ponderable dielectrics whereas according

[73]

to Maxwell there is displacement wherever there is electric force, whether
material bodies are present or not. Ether is as dielectric.

> "... in a dielectric under the influence of an electromotive
> force, we can assume that the electricity in each molecule is shifted so
> that one edge becomes positively charged and the other negatively, but
> the electricity remains attached to the molecule, and it does not pass
> through the one molecule in the other. This orientation of molecule
> charges appears in Maxwell as a current passage ...... Whittaker »

But how appeared the elastic fluid in dielectrics and ether?

Ether for Maxwell was "a pervading medium of small but real
density"

> "...When electromotive force acts on a dielectric it produces a
> state of polarization of its parts similar in distribution to the polarity of
> the parts of a mass of iron under the influence of magnet, or like the
> magnetic polarization, capable of being described as a state in which
> every particle has it's opposite poles in opposite condition...Maxwell'

What more natural then than to identify the structure of the ether with
that of material dielectrics and to postulate a charge polarization of it's parts
(ether's) under the influence of electromotive force by analogy with that of
material dielectrics. He conceived of the ether with the aid of an analogy of
the material dielectric.[22]

> "... For Faraday the displacement was applicable only to
> dielectric materials .. while according to Maxwell, displacement exists
> wherever there is electric power, whether there are material bodies or
> not ... Whittaker»
>
> «.... The Maxwell method involves the hypothesis that if an
> electric field is created then there is a displacement of electricity in
> both a dielectric medium and the conductors... Ramsey »

This etheric current, which Maxwell called the *displacement current,*
is supposed to produce the same magnetic effects as the normal current. From

---

[22] The structure of scientific inference, Mary B.Hesse California Press 1974

a mathematical point of view, it adds an additional term to the equations that before the Maxwell era described the electromagnetic changes, presupposing a new natural phenomenon.

> "... it becomes necessary to consider the vacuum, impregnated by a non-mechanical ether, whose atoms are electrically polarized ... Watson and Burbury»
>
> ... ether is the simplest possible dielectric type and consists of two types of tiny uncompressed elastic elements called negative and positive elements .. Barnett »
>
> "... all physicists after Maxwell agree to assign dielectric polarization to the ether ... Duhem"

So, the electric ether, is polarized by the electric fluid, which will later be identified with the luminiferous ether of optics.

> "... According to Faraday - Maxwell, the ether is polarizing just as matter ... Helmholtz»
>
> "... in fact this etheric polarization is something that still exists in the empty space without the presence of dielectrics or conductors, so it cannot possibly be attributed to an electric displacement. A dynamic theory of electromagnetic effects could yield the existence of this etheric shift, which has all the properties of the electric flow, without being the same electric flux, to the ether. The case is anyway experimentally correct and greatly simplifies the theory, and we will leave it at present as it is ... .Larmor »
>
> "... The theory of displacement currents on which all else was based, was not welcomed by the most distinguished physicists of the Maxwell era. Helmholtz eventually accepted it but after several years, and W. Thomson (Kelvin) never seemed to accept it until the end of his life, "Whittaker"

Thomson was a leader of the British scientific community at the time, and he simply didn't believe that such a thing as displacement current could exist.

[75]

"... it is obvious that the portion of the displacement current referring to the dielectric is a real current in the ordinary sense of the word. But it is otherwise with the current existing in the vacuum. Here is no interpretation that can be depicted and here lies what is the strictly new and hypothetical that Maxwell introduced to electrodynamics. Maxwell himself had no scruple as he treated ether or vacuum as an ordinary dielectric with k = 1 in explaining this part also by means of a displacement of electric charges, to suggest his interpretation of the displacement of electrical charges. Already with our current views it is very difficult to accept. It is better to confess openly that an interpretation of the displacement current in the vacuum is currently impossible ... Shaefer »

It follows from this that every electric current must form a closed circuit. The importance of this result will be seen when we investigate the laws of electromagnetics. Maxwell article 62 to Treatise. [23]

Comment

D' Abro in his study of the methodology of science[24] analyzes the criterion of simplicity: "when we consider the procedure of the scientist, we find that it consists in co-ordinating and linking together in a rational manner a number of experimental facts, with the **maximum of simplicity**...this criterion appears to be linked with our valuing of the expenditure of effort. Thus, even a dog finds it simpler to enter a house by the front door rather than clamber in through the back window....all human beings agree unanimously on those co-

---

[23] Indeed, this was posited to explain magnetic fields that are produced by changing electric fields. Displacement currents play a central role in the propagation of electromagnetic radiation, such as light and radio waves, through empty space.

[24] "the evolution of scientific thought" Dover p.359

ordinations which are regarded as the simplest, we may assume the urge towards simplicity to be fundamental...."

But the previous analysis of the electrical displacement of Maxwell, the two fluids, the elastic and the uncompressible, the dielectric polarizations, the displacement currents, etc. do not seem the simplest one that could be installed. Isn't the criteron of simplicity attributed more naturally, with the particle nature of electricity? But this not simple co-ordination, as Maxwell wrote, is important, **when we investigate the laws of electromagnetics and the theory of light.**

2.5 The   Maxwell's mathematics

Maxwell's four equations are based on the work of Coulomb, Ampere, Gauss, Neumann, and Faraday, and have been presented by Maxwell in a nine-year effort, from 1855 to 1864. In these equations he describes the fields connecting them with their sources, ρ and j (charges and currents), but does not describe how these fields affect another test charge that occurs in their range.

The first formulas of field electromagnetism equations prior to Maxwell's intervention was in integral form, in the constellation of dynamic lines and flows (surface and line integrals) according to the mathematics of the pioneers. Maxwell's intervention was only mathematical. We remember that E are fields generated by electric charges and B fields (magnetic) generated by electric currents, there are no stationary sources for them.

An example of the old equations

Gauss law in the base of lines of force of Faraday:

The total of the electric flux out of a closed surface is equal to the charge enclosed, divided by the permittivity

$$\iint E dS = q/\varepsilon$$

In the special case of a spherical surface with a charge at its center, the electric field is perpendicular to the surface, with the same measure at all points, giving the simple expression: $E = q / \varepsilon r^2$

That is, the dependence of the inverse square law of the electric field on Coulomb's law is derived from Gauss's law. This equation is one of Maxwell's four equations. In Gauss's law there are no electrostatic forces. But why is it true? Because it produces the Coulomb field that has described the force between charges (observable changes). If Coulomb's law did not exist, what experiment would we have to verify Gauss's law? What would describe the world of experience? It is the "*deepest essence of natural things*," says Maxwell.

The old theories laws were

$$\oint \vec{E} d\vec{l} = -\frac{d}{dt} \iint \vec{B} d\vec{S} \ldots\ldots(Faraday)\ldots\ldots(A1)$$

$$\oint \vec{B} d\vec{l} = \mu \iint \vec{j} d\vec{S} \ldots\ldots\ldots(Ampere)\ldots\ldots(A2)$$

$$\iint \vec{E} d\vec{S} = q/\varepsilon \ldots\ldots\ldots\ldots(Gauss)\ldots\ldots(A3)\ldots$$

$$\iint \vec{B} d\vec{S} = 0 \ldots\ldots\ldots\ldots\ldots\ldots\ldots\ldots\ldots(A4)$$

Maxwell was a theoretical physicist with a strong sense of intuition. His entire construction of the fields had an intuitive starting point, framed by mathematics.

The mathematical points on which **Maxwell based his mathematical leap** are two:

1. the subtle but substantial difference between the total and the partial derivative in time

2. the collolaries of the vector analysis

1. The first is the equation $\frac{dr}{dt} = \frac{\partial r}{\partial t} + w.\nabla r$

where w , is the velocity of an object located in space – e.g. a test-charged particle - and not a reference system.

[78]

Let f be any function pertaining to any particular moving particle. Then df/dt denotes its rate of change as the particle moves about; whereas $\partial f/\partial t$ will mean the local rate of change with the time. That is, the former denotes the time- rate of change of f, following the individual history of the particle, while the later denotes the time- rate of change at a fixed point of space(at a point given relatively to the reference system and not participating in the motion…A.O' Rahily electromagnetic theory page 4)

…the df/dt is obtained in the moving system with the particle.. L. Solymar "Lectures on Electrodynamics.

"… Maxwell developing his ideas, he detected everything in the medium, in the ether. In this image, we investigate areas that are permanently stationary in the ether and consider electrical charge as something that appears and disappears, increases or decreases within that region (volume, surface .. "(Swan)."

This in mathematics means partial derivative and 18th century (1786 Legendre)

So the total derivatives in old electricity equations become partial.

2. The properties used are two theorems of vector analysis, to study changes in flows through volumes, which eventually lead to points.

Divergence Theorem (Gauss): connects a double to a triple integral, in fact the flow A of a closed surface fluid S, with the flux divergence in the volume V surrounding the surface S

$$\iint A.\,dS = \iiint \nabla.\,AdV$$

The divergence theorem is employed in any <u>conservation law</u> which states that the volume total of all sinks and sources, that is the volume integral of the divergence, is equal to the net flow across the volume's boundary.

And Stokes theorem

Connects the line integral of the tangent component of a vector F round a closed curve C, to the surface integral of the vertical curl component of this vector at any surface S bounded by the closed curve C.

[79]

$$\oint_C \vec{F} \cdot d\vec{r} = \iint_S (\nabla \times \vec{F}) \cdot d\vec{S},$$

Then the classical equations were transformed into the field form in

$$\nabla \times \vec{E} = -\frac{\partial \vec{B}}{\partial t} \quad \text{......} (B.1.) \qquad \nabla \times \vec{B} = \mu \vec{j} \text{..........} (B.2.)$$

$$\nabla \vec{E} = \rho / \varepsilon \quad \text{..........} (B.3.) \qquad \nabla \vec{B} = 0 \quad \text{..............} (B.4.)$$

Now again Maxwell's intuition warned him of the lack of beauty in the above equations. He observed that Faraday's law B_1 and Ampère's law B_2 are strikingly similar, except that Ampère's law did not have this consequence, complementary to Faraday's law, in which a magnetic field changing over time can produce an electric field. Intuitive beauty would want in Amper's law, a time-varying electric field to produce a magnetic field.

In his wandering, he realized the **mathematical inconsistency of the equations..**

In relation (B$_2$), while the divergence of the first member is identically zero (vector analysis law), the same is not the case for the second member.

Why does divj $\neq 0$ apply in the general case?

Let us consider the flux of j from a closed surface in which encloses a volume V. This flow is equivalent to the flux of charges from the surface. If the **principle of conservation of charge** (which has been a cornerstone of electromagnetism since the beginning of the 19th century) applies, the flow of charges from the surface should be equal to the amount of charge reduction contained in the volume, that is, an equality between charge density and current density:

$$\iint_S \vec{j} dS = -\frac{\partial}{\partial t} \iiint_V \rho \, dV \quad \text{and from theorem of divergence}$$

$$\nabla \vec{j} = -\frac{\partial \rho}{\partial t} \quad \text{....} (1.1)$$

the famous **equation of continuity**.

The principle of continuity implies the eradication of all action at a distance such as is exemplified in Newton's law of gravitation. It is probable that a belief in the principle of continuity arises from the fact that in daily life all action seems to be transmitted by contact. Again, an object moves from "here" to "there" through a continuous series of intermediary positions. Physicists during the eighteenth and nineteenth centuries paid little heed to the principle.

Only when, as a result of Maxwell's discoveries, electromagnetic induction was found to be propagated by continuous action through a medium, did the popularity of the principle increased. This led to the field physics, to the discovery of a new category differing from matter, namely, the electromagnetic field. Einstein succeeded in placing gravitation on the same field basis as electromagnetic, in this way obviating Newton's action at a distance.

Now for Maxwell, equation (1.1) expresses the principle of charge conservation and divj = 0 applies only to the static case (the zero of the right member).

Again the inconsistency of Maxwell: In relation (B$_2$), while the divergence of the first member is identically zero (vector analysis law), the same is not the case for the second member.

With this inconsistency in mind, now consider (B$_3$) which if is solved for ρ, gives ρ = εdivE Therefore

$$\frac{\partial \rho}{\partial t} = \varepsilon \vec{\nabla} . \frac{\partial \vec{E}}{\partial t}$$

And replacing in (1.1) we have

$$\vec{\nabla} \vec{j} + \varepsilon \vec{\nabla} \frac{\partial \vec{E}}{\partial t} = 0 = \nabla (\vec{j} + \varepsilon \frac{\partial \vec{E}}{\partial t})$$

That is, the vector in parentheses is a circuital vector as a consequence of the principle of conservation of charge, and the law of Ampere (B$_2$) is supplemented

$$\nabla \times \vec{B} = \mu (\vec{j} + \varepsilon \frac{\partial \vec{E}}{\partial t}) \dots \dots (1.2)$$

[81]

So finally the Maxwell equations of electromagnetism are:

$$\nabla \times \vec{E} = -\frac{\partial \vec{B}}{\partial t} \ \dots (\Gamma.1) \qquad \nabla \times \vec{B} = \mu(\vec{j} + \varepsilon \frac{\partial \vec{E}}{\partial t}.) \dots (\Gamma.2)$$

$$\nabla . \vec{E} = \rho / \varepsilon \ \ \dots (\Gamma.3) \qquad \nabla . \vec{B} = 0 \qquad \dots (\Gamma.4)$$

with ε and μ are the permittivity   and permeability of free space.

2.6 The dual symmetry, the electromagnetic waves

This name, dual symmetry, is given to the invariance of Maxwell equations in a source free space, ($\rho = j = 0$), as to discreet transformations $E \rightarrow B \ \ and \ B \rightarrow -E$. In words if E and B are solutions to the source free Maxwell equations, dual symmetry implies that B´=E and E´=-B are solutions as well.

But   now we will see the imaginative operation of dual symmetry, with Maxwell's intuition.

Consider equations B_2 and Γ_2

The displacement current in the second member of Γ_2, - the last term - provides a mechanism where a time-varying electric field can create a magnetic field symmetric with Faraday's law, in which a time-varying magnetic field can produce a electric field (equation Γ_1)

So Maxwell made a theoretical conjecture and added this term to Ampère's law. It was Maxwell's famous displacement current that gave the full expression of Maxwell's equations, though it caused many problems in accepting the theory. Now the two laws would be almost exact mirror images to each other (mirror symmetry). Here was the redemptive dual symmetry of the laws of the electromagnetic field that satisfied Maxwell. But - continued Maxwell - while it was emotionally satisfying, did that mean anything? Maxwell played with the equations, to see what was going to happen. And what was happening, was magical!

[82]

The term displacement current says that a changing electric field (right side of Ampère's law, Γ_1) creates a magnetic field (left side of Γ_2's law). But Faraday's law, Γ_1 tells us that a changing magnetic field creates an electric field.

So Maxwell was intuitively wondering why couldn't the electric and magnetic fields, once properly adjusted, continue to operate the equations? Each one changes and creates the other in turn, going back and forth, so on by themselves, with absolutely nothing else to help them.

The answer is: that's exactly what they do. The mathematical result is electromagnetic radiation. **The fields of Maxwell of an accelerating charge, are propagated wavy!**

$$\nabla^2 E = \mu.\varepsilon \frac{\partial^2 E}{\partial t^2} \quad and \ \nabla^2 B = \mu.\varepsilon \frac{\partial^2 B}{\partial t^2}$$

with velocity $c = \frac{1}{\sqrt{\mu.\varepsilon}}$ which was equal to light velocity!

The values E and B in the above equations are represented by oscillations propagating in a space without currents and charges, where c represents the ratio between the electromagnetic to electrostatic charge unit and equals 3×10^{10}. Various types of radiation are included here, visible light, radio waves (used by our cell phone), microwaves (used in radar), x-rays (used in medicine) and so on. Whence it became necessary to assume that periodic perturbations in the strains and stresses of the field would be propagated in the form of waves through the ether with this particular speed. But this velocity was precisely that of light waves propagated through the luminiferous ether. The conclusion was obvious. Unless we were to assume that this coincidence was due to blind chance, we had to recognize that what we commonly called a ray of light was nothing else than e series of oscillations in the electromagnetic field, propagated from point to point. Electromagnetic waves and luminous waves, were thus all one. Hence for the two ethers , the electrical ether and the luminiferous ether, were seen to be the same continuum.

[83]

Maxwell mathematically predicted that light was really electromagnetic radiation. It was the most beautiful unification in physics: electromagnetic and optics.

Before the theory could be accepted it was necessary that Maxwell's hypothetical electromagnetic waves should be produced electrically in the laboratory. This turned out to be difficulty, the difficulty being not so much in producing them as in proving they had actually been produced. As the years went by and no such waves were detected, physicists began to have misgivings as to the validity of Maxwell ideas, especially since they were based on rather loose analogies. No matter how attractive Maxwell's theory might be on paper, it could at best be regarded as no more than an extremely interesting though rather dubious hypothesis, unless electromagnetic waves and their properties were investigated actually detected in the laboratory.

Maxwell did not live to see the vindication of his theory. It was not till seven years after his death that the electromagnetic waves he had predicted, were first detected by Hertz. Except the faint sparks crossing the gap in Hertz's simple loop in laboratory, Hertz proved that the disturbances exhibited reflection and refraction and other wave like characteristics, and measured their wave length, yet these moved with the speed of light, and this is Maxwell's famous prophecy: "Light may be ultimately an electromagnetic wave."

The displacement current was the only Maxwell's contribution to the four equations named after him. Maxwell was not an experimenter, but a theoretician, and a deep mathematician. He saw the relationship between the laws of Ampere, Faraday and Gauss and realized that there was a gap to fill the chain. It had been shown that a circuit with a capacitor kept the current open, while no current passed through the capacitor, even though there was a magnetic field in the space between its arms. Thus the law of Ampere seemed invalid. The experiment, however, had shown that the currents were producing the magnetic fields. Maxwell, guided by the mathematical path we have developed, to interpret the extra term answered the problem by assuming that a current was in fact passing through the capacitor called the displacement current. This appeared to be the rate of change of the electric field between the capacitor plates. This flow enabled Maxwell to combine all the laws into one mathematical set. There is really no electromagnetic phenomenon that can be interpreted in the context of his theory without the displacement current.

2.7 the propagated potentials

Long before Hertz's discoveries, in the years of the great controversy between theories of electromagnetism, appeared the first different 'interpretation' of Maxwell's equations through another mathematical construction that closed the logical gap between the polarity of ether and the displacement current, ending up with the same equations for the fields! This construction was done with the potentials A and φ.

We know that the potential in electrostatics is a function to find the vector of the field where we are interested. It is a useful conception because it is easy to calculate the field from the load distribution ρ to volume υ by solving the Poisson equation and is (the solution)

$\varphi_P(t) = \int d\upsilon \, \rho(t)/r$ for each time point t ...... (1)

by which we calculate the electrostatic field with much simpler steps than the calculation of E. This scalar quantity, the Neumann's 'order,[25] in any electrical or other conservation system, is like an imaginary energy storage of which the action that moves the charges is derived through E = -divφ..

The vector potential A (Neumann)for the magnetic field of currents has the same characteristics, and the solution (after some mathematical complexity) is

$A = \int d\upsilon \, j(t)/r$ ....(2)   for every instant t

---

[25] Potential is an order given and transmitted from one point and received and executed by another. We assume that this order takes some time to reach from the broadcasting site to the reception site... ..**C. Neunann** That's exactly what Lorenz proved

The existence of a vector (instead of a scalar) for the potential of the magnetic field from which we derive the field, (B = curlA), is only a mathematical necessity (divB = 0)

In July 1867, in Poggenderff's Annalen Magazine, Ludvig Lorenz (different of H.A. Lorentz of electron theory) produced a new model of Maxwell's theory, as happened in case of mechanics, highlighting its different possibilities of interpretation.

The reader can find in text books that in the dynamic fields in the empty space, the Maxwell equations can be replaced by the equivalent "potential equations".

B=∇×A , E= -∇φ -∂A/∂t, dalA= -4πj dal φ= - 4πρ ......(3)

Where dal=$\nabla^2 - 1/c^2 \, \partial^2 / \partial t^2$

That is, by expressing the fields E and H as functions of potentials, Maxwell's equations become (3).

> "Equations that come from a purely empirical way are not necessarily exact expressions of real physical law. ... and it will always be possible to give the equations another form, always provided that these changes do not cause a noticeable change in the results obtained from the experiment ...... L.Lorenz»

Conversely in 1897 Levi-Civita produced from (3) the equations of Maxwell without any reference to the displacement current. (O'Rahily)

Thus the equivalence of Maxwell's equations (in vacuum), and (3), is mathematically complete!

the interpretations

Now, this mathematical intervention, is the second in the empirical laws of electricity, and as the first (Maxwell) began to question, and an ongoing "electrical literature" about its physical content. First were the fields, now the potentials.

..... So we see that the field equations are correct regardless of Maxwell's theory of displacement. That is, the Maxwell equations are a consistent scheme regardless of the truth of the assumptions from which they came. The theory of displacement can only be regarded as a presentation, and Maxwell's theory as the theory expressed by equations regardless of the physical interpretation that can be given to the various terms of these equations ... We can if we want to overlook Maxwell's interpretation ... **.Jeans**

This is a strange reference, from those who cultivate the climate that mathematical equations are superior to physical reality. Something like Maxwell's equations is the mathematical theory of electromagnetism (pure mathematics) and Maxwell's and Lorentz's interpretations of the mathematical models. The equations apply regardless of the physical interpretation of their terms, we do not know what physical reality they describe (ether). Maxwell's famous "scaffolding" for building his theory was the mathematical reasoning!

But in the context of field electricity, we will again be "looking" to "define" what is being propagated in Lorenz equations.

"... The potential that was formerly only a type of calculus, with Faraday becoming the real link in space, the cause of the action of forces ... .. Boltzmann"

"... For Maxwell the potential A was not a mere mathematical auxiliary quantity, but a function of the situation with special significance.... Wiechert »

"... .The vector potential, instead of a analytic invention, represents the most important physical property of the system ... .. J.J.Thomson"

"... the electric potential, which is proportional to temperature, is a scientific concept, we have no reason to regard it as a physical state .... Maxwell."

[87]

"In the theories of propagation of electric actions proposed by Lorenz and Riemann, what crosses the space is no longer a reality, but something fantastic, a mathematical symbol ... Maxwell's ideas have nothing to do with these dogmas. Mathematical symbols are not propagated. Thus the potential function is Σq (t)/ r and not Σq (t-r /c) / r as Riemann's case asserts. What is spreading every time is a real amount of conduction flow in the conductors and the displacement flow in the dielectrics..Duhem ..

It is weird that Duhem talks about a real shift of displacement, since it has never been measured! . Is not distinguished in the flux of displacement, the metaphysical component of   physical theory   that him (Duhem) has proclaimed?

All the above descriptions, however, are simplified in the name of ' virtue of reality'

...So it seems more reasonable to study them   -the equations of Maxwell- regardless of how they were produced, to view them as hypothetical assumptions, and to depend on their validity for the large number of natural laws they cover. If we think so, we can get rid of a large number of auxiliary concepts that make Maxwell's theory more difficult, because these concepts actually make no sense if we finally exclude the concept of direct action from a distance .... Hertz

This quote from Hertz is the most critical. Hertz negotiates everything except the contact action model. But this too will not be excluded. It seems that contact action is a distance action that spreads at a finite speed and gives the impression of contact. We will see it again later.

... .The field equations, at least in the form that apply to simple cases, appear to be more certain than the ideas through which a basis for them has been more or less successfully constructed ... H.Lorentz

Maxwell's equations are *"knowledge by revelation"* only that revelation is mathematical revelation.

[88]

What exactly are the potentials? This is a philosophical question. The potential at one point in the field, is the ability to exert electrical force at that point, and it is actually exerted when we carry a receiver charge at that point. With this image the potential is the most precise ontological characteristic of the field, which exerts E and B forces only when receiver charges appear, and is itself a **potential reality**. Field means potential and potential means field. When the source charge varies, the potential at each point in the field varies, and mathematics proves (in next chapter) that these changes are propagated at a finite speed. And mathematical description is the only valid description for a "potential reality". Or, the answer is in quantum mechanics where we speak of one-dimensional step potential as an idealized system used to model incident, reflected and transmitted matter waves. (Wikipedia)

2.8 The retarded potentials

The first characteristic of these equations is that there is no term that Maxwell interpreted as a displacement current. There is no mention of ether.

The current that meets the law of Ampere is not

the conduction current + displacement current

but only the conductive current whose density we consider to be propagated. But Lorenz's theory of propagating potentials has even more serious consequences. If we solve the last differential (wave) equations of (1) we have that

$\varphi_P(t) = \int dn\, \rho(t-r/c)/r$ and $A_P(t) = \int dr\, j(t-r/c)/cr$ (1)

are the formulas of Ludvig Lorenz for potentials called retarded potentials.

These solutions show that the perturbations φ and A are propagated in all directions at a speed equal to the speed of light, symbolized in the literature

$\phi = \int dr\, [\rho]/r \qquad \kappa\alpha\iota \qquad A = \int dr[\,j\,]/cr$ [26]..........(5)

and are interpreted as: If we want to calculate A and ϕ at point P at time t we have to consider the density of charge $[\rho]$ or current $[j]$ at the volume element dr at distance r from P, at time moment t-r/c and not αt moment t, with c the speed of electromagnetic radiation in space. It is the knowledge of these potentials that provides us the E and H of Maxwell's theory. The potential 'here and now' equals the potential 'there and then'.

This result of Lorenz is reminiscent of a reference to Riemann from 1858 (and Gauss's insistence on the propagation of electromagnetic actions at finite speeds)

"... I have found that the electrodynamics effects between the currents can be interpreted as assuming that the action of an electric mass with the rest, is not instantaneous but propagates at a constant speed, which within the limits of observation is equal to the speed of light... .Riemann »

Lorenz finally confirms it with his formulas: If we want to express the potentials with respect to charges and currents, so that the fields resulting from these potentials are the same as the fields of Maxwell's equations, the potentials must be propagated, at a finite speed.

"... these new equations further express that the overall action between free electricity and currents takes time to propagate - a hypothesis not at all strange to science, which can be assumed to have a high probability of occurring. According to the formulas that result, the action at point (x, ψ, ζ) at time t does not depend on the simultaneous action at point (x´, $\psi´$, $\zeta´$) but on its condition at time r/c that is, before the time required to travel the distance r at a constant speed c ... this theoretical conclusion is that electrical forces take time to propagate, these forces are apparently only act from a distance ... and that any action or electrical currents in fact depends on the

---

[26] Brackets represent retarded symbols.

condition to the information of the immediate environment ... L.Lorenz »

"... it is characteristic of the theory that it considers a propagation of electrodynamics disturbances at the speed of light in free ether. Here is the speculation that it is possible to symbolize the disorder at any point as a consequence elsewhere in the past as corresponding to the rate of propagation. Since we consider that all ethereal disturbances are born of electric particles, we assume that it is also possible to refer to the process exclusively to these particles as we did in old theories ... .. Wiechert »

Essentially the difference between the two interpretations is exactly this: Maxwell sets $j+ j+\partial E/\partial t$ and considers actions as instantaneous; Lorenz for j sets [j] and actions propagated. The famous displacement stream that created so many problems, is being abolished with only a change in the idea of propagations of actions.

This eliminates the materialization of electricity, leaving the active fields of forces

... The main difficulty of what is meant by electric displacement and the displacement current is now eliminated, because this unknown current is merely a mathematical substitute for the propagated potential... ..Macdonald

The displacement current is mathematical current!

... We can find the basic principles of Maxwell's theory starting from classical laws. It is enough to supplement them with the assumption that remote actions are spreading at a finite speed... .Civita

That is, a lot of fighting for nothing!

"... in Maxwell's theory, we have in our minds the state of matter or medium by which the field is filled. But while we are talking about this situation we must immediately point out the strange fact that, although we never overlook it, we should not try to form a picture of it, and in fact we can say nothing about it! It is true that we must

[91]

symbolize the internal pressures in the medium, round an electric field or a magnet, that we must think of electricity as some substance or fluid, free to move in ducts and limited to equilibrium positions in dielectrics, and that we also mean the magnetic field as a result of invisible motions e.g. rotation of dynamic lines ... But this should not be considered as absolutely necessary. We can extend the theory to a large extent and explain a large number of phenomena, without engaging in such meditations... .H.Lorentz »

So it is obvious that as long as E and H are true, so are A and φ. It turns out that something is propagated but we do not discern what it is, the two developments are equivalent, the energy propagated is the energy of the field that generates it or the energy that generates the field. This is illustrated in the excerpt below, which challenges the reality of all these symbols.

"... there seems to be no need inherent in the requirements of this model itself, that all mathematical constructions must correspond to identifiable processes in the physical system. This is because there is no longer any reason for the symbols appearing in the fundamental mathematical equations to have their natural counterparts, and why the use of purely auxiliary mathematical quantities should not be prevented from simplifying mathematical proofs ... Bridgman. "

Today the entire scientific community has adopted Lorenz's view, using the retarded potentials and pushing as useless the Maxwell displacement current.

epilogue

So, Maxwell equations may be written in many different forms: in different units, in integral form, with quaternions, in terms of geometrical algebra, etc, But it is convenient to write them in the "potential" form in order to connect later with QED. The equations are expressed succinctly by using the magnetic "vector potential **A** and the scalar electric potential V.

".....It is important to remember that electric and magnetic fields are not directly observed in any experiments; only phenomena in material bodies are observed. The existence of fields in the space surrounding charges is assumed because phenomena can be conveniently described or explained by means of this assumption. In the electron theory we assume the existence of these fields, but we do not attempt to explain how they are produced or what they consist of. We may if we like regard them as merely auxiliary mathematical quantities introduced into the theory for convenience in attempting to describe phenomena. Most physicists, however, believe that these fields really exist. It has been suggested that electric and magnetic fields are modifications of the ether, a medium filling all space. The hypothesis is not of much use; it is sufficient to suppose that the charges excite the fields in the surrounding space...*H.A.Wilson Modern Physics 1928* (O' Rahily p.225)"

PART THREE: ELECTRONS AND ETHER, THE SYMBIOSIS

PART THREE: ELECTRONS AND ETHER, THE SYMBIOSIS

the electron brought a hurricane to electromagnetism

3.1 Atomism in electricity, the electron

The electrolysis, and Millikan experiments, install into physics the image of atomism in electricity.

Electrolysis is the chemical deposition of a compound into its constituent elements brought about by a flow of electric current.

Direct current is passed through the compound (the compound can be in molten or aqueous state).

Electrical energy (from the direct current) is changed into chemical energy (the decomposition of the compound).

One common example is the electrolysis of water, where water decomposes to hydrogen and oxygen.

Even when the experiment revealed the most characteristic phenomenon of atomism in electricity, electrolysis, studied by Faraday himself and interpreted by Clausius in 1857, the British attachment to Newtonian doctrine left no room to them for another image of electricity than that of fluid and continuous medium. Faraday's ideas of a current were of the vaguest:

".. by a current, I mean anything progressive, whether it be a fluid of electricity or two fluids moving on opposite directions, or merely vibrations, or speaking more generally, progressive forces"

Maxwell, admitted the heuristic and pedagogic convenience of atomism, but entirely temporary.

"suppose however we assert the fact of the constant value of the molecular charge in the ions within the electrolyte are actually

[94]

charged with certain definite quantities of electricity one molecule of electricity. This phrase-gross as it is and out of harmony with the rest of this treatise will enable us at least to state clearly what is known about electrolysis. It is extremely improbable however that , when we come to understand the true nature of electrolysis, we shall retain in any form the theory of molecular charges…**Maxwell"**

So the adoption of individual electricity is significantly delayed ...

"... even if the nature of the particles in the cathode discharge was not detected, and if the Zeeman effect had never been discovered, the facts known to Faraday and Maxwell were sufficient to demonstrate that no other conception of electricity than atomic one, not logically self-consistent ... **Joseph Larmor** »

Whittaker describes the evolution

"… The tendency which is now general, that is, to abandon Weber's electron theory in favour of Maxwell's theory, involved certain changes in the conception of electric charge. In Weber's theory, electrical phenomena were attributed to stationary or moving charges, which could most readily **be pictured** as having a discrete and atom-like existence. The conception of displacement, on the other hand, which lay at the root of Maxwell's theory, was more in harmony with the representation of electricity as something of a continuous nature. And as Maxwell's views met with increasing acceptance, the atomistic hypothesis seem to have entered on a period of decay ... "

For all that, it's hard to see what the other British Kelvin tells us

".. I prefer to accept an individual theory of electricity, as provided by Faraday and Maxwell and finally proposed by Helmholtz in his last lecture at the Royal Institute, and has been widely accepted by theoretical researchers and teachers ..." .

And all this in 1897, when in 1846 Weber's first electron theory was proposed. The British seem to erase the science of continental Europe.

Maxwell's followers turned to the idea of the atomic nature of electricity after Helmholtz's famous 1881 lecture *"on the modern development*

[95]

of Faraday's conceptions of electricity" exploring electrolysis phenomena, according to the latest discoveries of chemistry and Faraday's law of electrochemical equivalence.

"... We do not yet have another theory that explains all chemical phenomena so simply and so consistently, from the atomic theory developed in modern chemistry ... if we assume that substances are made of atoms, we cannot avoid the conclusion that electricity, both positive and negative, is divided into defined elementary parts, which behave like atoms of electricity. As long as the ion moves in the electrolytic fluid, it remains attached to its electric equivalent. In the surface of the electrodes breaks down, as long as there is sufficient electric power, the ions discharge their electrical charges and become electrically neutral... .Helmotz »

This was the first ideological "blow" to the British school of theoretical physics, which disputed, almost useless, the physical existence of the Maxwell field, the dynamic lines and all that these concepts produced.

Since then, as Schuster observes

"... The electricity molecule triumphed and Maxwell's apostles, who had long insisted on denying it, had to harmonize their views with it."

And this was done by rewriting even the history, as A. O 'Rahily points out in presenting an excerpt from British Lord Rutherford:

"... Following Faraday's classical experiments on electrolysis, the idea that electricity such as matter was atomic in structure was proposed by Maxwell and after by Weber"

Then in August 1897 J.J. Thomson, a professor at the University of Cambridge, wrote his famous work *"On Testing the Theory of Electric Particles"* in which he described his famous experiments in determining the charge-to-mass ratio (q/m) of the particles comprising the cathode rays. *This ratio connects electricity with matter.*

[96]

Later American physicist Robert Millikan proved that electricity has a truly atomic structure, something that scientists only knew in theory. In order to prove this, it was necessary to verify not only that electricity was present in all experiments as an integer multiple of the charge unit, but also that this unit is not an average value, as it was shown, for example, in atomic weights. In other words, it was necessary to measure the charge of a single ion with such a degree of accuracy that would allow Millikan to verify that this charge was always the same. The same had to be proved in the case of free electrons.

In 1906 he began devising a series of improvements to Thomson's experiment, which led him to discover the device by dropping oil drops. This device accurately measured the electron charge in 1911.

Subsequently studying the phenomena of electrolytic conductivity, gas conductivity and metal conductivity, with numerous experiments and new discoveries, the individuality of electricity became undisputed.

In 1909, more information about the electron was uncovered by Millikan via his "oil drop" experiments. Millikan created microscopic oil droplets, which could be electrically charged by friction as they formed or by using X-rays. These droplets initially fell due to gravity, but their downward progress could be slowed or even reversed by an electric field lower in the apparatus. By adjusting the electric field strength and making careful measurements and appropriate calculations, Millikan was able to determine the charge on individual drops

" ... The electrons were discovered in 1895 as particles. You can count them. You can put them on a drop of oil and measure their load. Over time it has been found that electricity in metal wires is nothing more than an electron motion ... Feynman »

But this image of the electron cannot be reconciled with the image of the displacement current in the Maxwell ether. If we eliminate this fluid, all mathematical construction collapses. What is the natural meaning of div and rot of vectors without fluid? but let's wait!

> "... we are convinced that a purely mathematical justification can never guarantee physical results, that everything in physics comes from mathematics, it must be restored to another form. Our problem is to find where physics goes into general theory...Bridgman »

The conflict between the two views, the atomic and continuous nature of electricity, continued for many years to impede the recognition of the individuality of electricity. The situation is depicted in a French text by Chappuis-Lamotte expressing in 1911, a condition that is still maintained.

> "... These new phenomena have had the great effect of causing to some degree a return to the old ideas ... The theory of electron for the time being seems to interpret most phenomena. It has not yet taken a definitive form. So in our presentation we will hold Maxwell's theory and only refer to the theory of electron, in the study of some phenomena where its use is appropriate ... "

3.2 The theory of Hertz

Matter in motion through the ether drag the ether in its interior

With the development of the field theory, the ether problem took an unexpected turn. For Maxwell ether had purely mechanical properties, more complex than those of known matter. But neither Maxwell nor his successors were able to describe a satisfactory mechanical model to interpret the laws of Maxwell's electromagnetic field. The laws (the field equations) were simple and clear and the mechanical interpretations vague and contradictory.

Thus physicists gradually became accustomed to accepting electric and magnetic forces as fundamental concepts alongside those of mechanics, without requiring a mechanistic interpretation of them. The purely mechanistic view of nature slowly began to drop.

"... the view that wants mechanics as the basis of the rest of the physics disciplines and interprets all physical phenomena based on mechanistic ideas is a bias ... .Ernst Mach"

This change led to a new, second division for the whole of physics, because the overcoming of matter was of fundamental physical and philosophical importance, the material reality being "like a confession of faith" to the majority of physicists. But this change led to a fundamental dualism which in the long-run was insupportable. **Were these mechanistic categories supposed to describe the whole of physics or the electromagnetic respectively?** it was the relation between electricity and matter, and we have historically called this the **"ether crisis"**.

This dualism still confronts us in unextenuated form in the theory of Hertz, where matter appears not only as the bearer of velocities, kinetic energy, and mechanical pressures, but also as the bearer of electromagnetic fields.

According to Hertz, - *electrodynamics of moving bodies*- the ether that is the carrier of electromagnetic activity is not described by any parameter in Maxwell's equations. If ether is immobile, what is it that differentiates electrical activity between immobile and moving bodies?

But the movements of ether do exist and are made through the material bodies of the system, which drug it. In matter it participates in its motion (w≠0), but in the empty space it has a definite velocity. There is no fundamental difference between the Hertz ether and the weighted matter, which exists in parts in the ether. Matter and ether are together carriers of the field. All of Maxwell's phenomena refer to immobile ether. For Hertz, they are also obtained in a moving body at a speed w through ether, which will change them as the wind speed changes the data of the sound phenomena. Now, from the relation

$$\frac{d}{dt} = \frac{\partial}{\partial t} + w.\nabla \quad \text{(the Maxwell mathematics, PART TWO)}$$

the change in E manifested by the electric force on a charged body is not only due to the change in the Maxwellian field but also to the motion of the body! (electrodynamics of moving particles at speed w) Also, a moving dielectric would create a magnetic field after transporting ether with it. In the two theories are $\rho = \rho'$,

A moving ether - this is a mechanical class - through matter connects the field of Maxwell to a moving carrier material. The $\frac{\partial E}{\partial t}$ will be detected by the change of E over the material carrier and when this carrier moves, the $\frac{\partial E}{\partial t}$ becomes dE/dt is that is Galilean invariant, that is, the equations of Maxwell's when they changed to contain a total instead of a partial derivative, fulfilled the Newtonian principle of relativity!

Total derivative in Galilean transformations

If w the velocity of the body carrier of the magnitude we study, the in

S we have $\frac{d}{dt} = \frac{\partial}{\partial t} + w.\nabla$ but w'=w-v so in S' we have

$$\left(\frac{d}{dt}\right)' = \left(\frac{\partial}{\partial t} + w.\nabla\right)' = \frac{\partial}{\partial t'} + w'\nabla' = \frac{\partial}{\partial t} + v.\nabla + (w-v).\nabla = \frac{\partial}{\partial t} + w.\nabla = (\frac{d}{dt}).$$

The subsequent Lorentz transformations and the theory of special relativity would no longer be needed.

However, this interpretation by Hertz led to erroneous results that contradicted experimental observations. e.g Fizeau measured the speed of light in moving water. If the ether were moving at the velocity of the water, having drifted away from it, the velocity of light had to be added to the velocity of the water, as the velocity of the wind to the velocity of sound. But the experiment showed that the velocities were not cumulative, yet the creation of a magnetic field by a charged rotating dielectric through the dragged ether, was never verified in the laboratory. Hertz's formalism was never used by subsequent scholars, nor was recognized the importance of the view for the invariance of

Maxwell's equations, changing perhaps the physical meaning of the parameter w, that is Hertz could not bring out Herzian's field significance.

Thomas Phipps, the physicist who refined the Hertzian theory in a new-Hertzian interpretation by attributing the ether velocity to the velocity of the test charge, writes:

> "But it seems regrettable that Hertz's Galilean invariant theory was rejected without mentioning its mathematical advantages while Maxwell's unalterable special case was maintained with only a reason for its mathematical advantages, and became the basis for all. Put differently, the illegitimate Maxwell's ethereal 'physics' was rejected by keeping it's invariants mathematics, while Hertz's invariant mathematics were rejected only to eliminate his illegitimate ether's 'physics'. We believe that it is never too late to remedy this strange situation in the political history of science… .T.Phipps »

3.3 A. Lorentz's Electromagnetic theory (1892)

A sphere is contracted in the direction of it's motion through the ether

After Maxwell described the electromagnetic field and it's motion, through the ether, Lorentz found the force that this field exerted on the

electrified bodies. Now the field theory is complete and we can call it Maxwell-Lorentz theory. Lorentz banished any form of ether dragging, and finally Einstein's (1905) theory of special relativity doesn't contain the ether as a mechanical medium at all.

The theory of Lorentz is based on two assumptions: that the ether is firmly fixed in space- that is to say, unable to move at all- and that electricity is firmly lodged in mobile elementary perticles.

In contradiction to Hertz, Lorentz assumed that the ether was never disturbed by the motion of matter; and just as in Maxwell's theory , a luminous source in motion through the ether would never communicate its velocity to the light waves it emitted, as we have seen, holding to his view of the FitzGerald attraction, assuming the electron to contract more and more as its speed through the ether increased.

If the atomism of electricity were to be linked to the field theory, the electron would have to be connected to ether, since electrons and ether were the substrates of the two theories. But in Lorenz's theory, there was a division of roles within the dualism of matter and field: the ether lost its mechanical properties and matter lost its electrical properties. Electrons carry only the charge which has a continuous distribution in extremely small but finite dimensions, and the ether is everywhere in and out of matter describing the electromagnetic phenomena with Maxwell's equations for space, exerting mechanical forces on the electron. (Maxwell -Lorentz equations)

Lorentz's ether was rigid, non-deformable, immobile, and thus defined as the system of reference to absolute tranquility, another name for Newton's absolute space. It did not fulfill the mechanical properties of matter, it has assumed the electromagnetic expression of the fields. These ether, traits automatically rule out the possibility of considering the field as a result of shifts or trends or modifications of any of our familiar form. On the other hand, the electrons collect the entire mechanical description of the system with a unique electrical property of charge. Thus Lorentz's theory delineates the landscape of the known dualistic conception.

> "… It was Lorentz's big breakthrough. All known phenomena of electromagnetism can be interpreted on the basis of two hypotheses: that the ether is firmly fixed in space - that is, it does not move at all - and that electricity is firmly integrated into the moving elementary particles. Today this discovery can be expressed as follows: physical space and ether are just different terms for the same thing, fields are natural conditions of space… ..Einstein »

[102]

The field and the electrons are not completely independent because the presence and motion of the electrons affect the field. And conversely the field, although considered non-mechanical, exerts forces on the electrons. The mechanical force exerted by the field on the electron is called by Lorentz, the "moving motion" force. Its mathematical expression results from the appropriate combination of electric and magnetic field sizes. The Lorentz force therefore behaves and acts as a link between the field and the mechanical electrons.

In Lorenz the continuity of the fields is not interrupted by the electron charges

"... for the charge distribution of the electron, we assume that it is distributed over an area of space, that is, all the volume occupied by the electron, and we consider the density of p as a constant function of the coordinates, so that the charged particle has no specific boundaries, but is surrounded by a thin layer in which the density gradually changes from the value inside the electron to the value zero" Lorentz.

The charge, that is, of the electrons coexists with the constant of ether, and there are forces within the Maxwell field. This keeps the field view of electricity in keeping with its individuality!

"The electrons within the matter of the dielectrics can be displaced by an electric force exerted by the ether, which we consider penetrates into any material body. In any case, this (known electric) displacement will immediately develop a new force by which the particle will return to its original position, which we call force - elastic force. The movement of electrons in dielectrics such as glass, controlled by tensile strength at specific mass boundaries by changing the electric shift of the ether itself, is what Maxwell called Lorentz displacement current. "Lorentz

From the references we understand that the ether-medium not only fills the entire space between molecules, electrons or atoms, but penetrates and permeates all of these bodies, exerting forces on the loads adapted to the particles, but without moving itself. The movement of a charged body is not

[103]

related to the ether that surrounds it, even to the ether that enters its molecules. No portion of the ether is in relative motion with another portion. Ether is motionless in Newton's absolute space, and only bodies with or without charge travel within it, which passes through it. We have again in the physical (after absolute space) a still and conceivable **Aristotelian first mover**, the ether-medium, which moves the charged particles, being immobile.

> "... indeed the most important of our fundamental assumptions must be that ether not only occupies all the space between the molecules, but impregnates all of these particles. We will also assume that, although the particles can and do move, the ether always remains calm. We will understand this initially frightening idea, considering the particles of matter as some local modification to the ether state. These modifications can of course travel through space while the volume elements of the medium in which they exist remain calm...
> ..Lorentz »

3.4 The electromagnetic force of Lorentz

The crucial point for reconciling the individuality of electricity and the continuous field electricity was the interaction of the two. Lorentz's force describes the forces exerted by an electromagnetic field on an electron. Through these forces E and B will be defined in terms of these forces acting on a test charge q and mass m moving at a velocity v at the point of the field. Lorentz's hypothesis was that the electron was a shell that when observed in a calming reference system it is spherical. The shell has a continuous load distribution. The entire force on the particle of electric charge q moving with velocity v through an electric field E and magnetic field B is defined by Lorentz as

$q\{E+(v \times H)\}. \dots(3.1)$

with the speed v in question was the speed of the electron through the

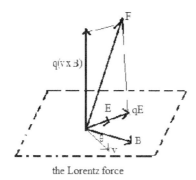

the Lorentz force

stagnant ether; whereas in Einstein's theory it is merely the speed with respect to any inertial system..

> ... .The first term qE represents the force exerted on the electron within the electrostatic field. In this case, the power per charge unit must be determined entirely by electrical displacement. This is the electric power ... Lorentz

The second term q × B is the magnetic force applied to the electron, and from this we derive the Laplace force $F = i \, (l \times B)$ that exerts the magnetic field on a linear stationary l-length conductor.

> "... having considered $F_1 = q \, E$, $F_2 = (qv \times B)$, the two are now combined in the way shown in the equation, considering beyond the immediate results of experiments, the assumption that generally the two forces coexist at the same time. ... Lorentz »

So Maxwell-Lorentz electricity has obtained five equations. Lorentz force is a contact force such as the racket pushes the ball, the field becomes a racket function, the ether connects the electron to the surrounding space since it is half matter and half charge, the force is exerted by the outer ether on all the internal points of the electrons in which there is a charge, and the most interesting results are given by the magnetic component of the force, since:

The electric field can vary the speed (kinetic energy) of the charged particle (force in a stationary body). On the contrary, the magnetic field can see that it can only change the direction of a charged particle and not its kinetic energy.

The magnetic force when applied to a charge has applications to particle accelerators such as the circulator, we use this effect where the magnetic field curves the particle's orbit, and a synchronized electric field at each rotation gives the particle an additional kinetic energy, which forces it to erase larger orbits, and when it has the energy it desires, it is extracted and used in various ways to study the properties of matter still for medical purposes. methods in the treatment of cancer. Even magnetic forces on power lines (Laplace power) are used to convert electricity into work, for example in electric motors where socket loops are used.

But we will note a theoretical paradox: the Lorentz force does not apply Newton's third law, which we have seen applies to electrostatic and Ampere force.

Yet another problematic factor behind all the changes in electrodynamics **is the term "velocity"**.

Obviously , velocity is not an intrinsic property of a body. **Velocity here (3.1) is a velocity relative to the immobile ether in the universe , it is an ablolute velocity** Unfortunately, most text books do not specify the velocity relative to what: relative the laboratory, relative to a magnet relative to an observer...

"..The rate of change in the position of the bodies between them is the only observable quantity relevant to our description of the natural world... ..F. A Lindemann »

... the velocity in Lorentz force is the velocity of the charge relative to the system of instruments used to measure the forces..Richardson »

[106]

"... in the Lorentz formula the velocity is relative to the tranquil ether or - preferably - to a system with fixed axes relative to the observer. ... Schott »

Here Schott says exactly that, the lab has always been a part of the medium for which the calculations were made, which did not differ from it.

".... We have so far not made a clear distinction between the notion of ethereal tranquility and the walls of a lab. .... Jean »

but Richardson clarifies the issue for all physics after the abolition of absolute space:

"...all results depend on the relative motion of matter ... the field of electrical theory which studies the properties of electric charges at rest is called electrostatics ... when we say at rest we mean in relation to each other. There is no verification of the view that the absolute movement of charges affects the action between them ... Richardson »

The same formula (3.1) will change velocity's reference in relativity , as ether is intangible.

3.5 Mechanics and electricity

But the ether crisis continues. It was the outlet to the reverse course, that is, the reduction of the principles of mechanics to those of electricity, where molecular electrons and protons had to be built only from electromagnetic quantities.

Abraham, (1902) Abraham, argued that whereas Lorentz's contractile electron called for the explicit addition of non-electromagnetic stabilizing forces, he, Abraham, could simply take the rigidity of his own spherical electron as a given and proceed from there without ever running into trouble.

In Abraham, we owe this first attempt, focused on the mechanical concept of mass. He assumed that the electron was a rigid sphere with a charge divided evenly around its surface and showed that the total mass of the moving electron could be constructed from the field sizes. Mass in this sense was

[107]

basically an electromagnetic event. Since the movement of the electron through the field was the factor that created its mass, an electron at rest would not have mass. Abraham's model was competing with that developed by Hendrik Lorentz (1899, 1904) and Albert Einstein (1905) which seem to have become more widely accepted; nevertheless, Abraham never gave up his model, since he considered it was based on "common sense".

If all mass of the electron could be ascribed to the interaction of the electron's charge with electromagnetic fields, then one could hope to build a consistent and universal physics based on electrodynamics. Abraham's approach was to calculate the inertia due to the self-induction of the electron as it moved through its own field and the induction due to any external field in which the electron found itself. One could compare the results thus obtained with Kaufmann's results, and if agreement was substantial, then it could be said with some assurance *that the mass of the electron was purely electromagnetic.*

Finally, in 1906. **Kaufmann** undertook a new set of measurements in the hopes of distinguishing between Abraham's theory and those of Lorentz and Einstein. By photographing the paths followed by the electrons, he reported that his experiments supported the Abraham theory. But still more precise experiments conducted by **Bucherer** reversed the verdict, and little doupt remained that the electron suffered the FitzGerald contraction in the precise degree demanded by Lorentz. Although Kaufmann's work was later criticized on methodological grounds, and later experiments (Bucherer) vindicated the Lorentz and Einstein predictions, opponents of the theory of relativity, often cited Abraham's theory and Kaufmann's data as evidence against Einstein's special theory.

Experiments were soon devised to test the opposing theories. The most accurate of these were those of **Bucherer** who favoured Lorentz's predictions. As a result, Abraham's pure field theory was abandoned. But even if Abraham's views were supported by the experiment, other difficulties would pave the way for pure field theories. For example, the electric charges on the

[108]

surface of an electron or inside it, being homogeneous, would repel each other and the electron would dissolve. To justify the stability of the electron we have to assume some intense exogenous pressure exerted on the escaping charges. But this pressure (**Poincaré pressure**) cannot be based on the field quantities of Maxwell and Lorenz, so it must be of non-electromagnetic origin. The electromagnetic field alone is therefore incapable of explaining the stability and existence of the electron. For these reasons, and for many others, any pure field theory based on the Lorentz-Maxwell electromagnetic field seems doomed to fail from the beginning. A more successful attempt was made by **Mie** later, and at some point **Weyl** seemed to prefer Mie's theory. But then he ignored it. In the face of these failures, physicists have reverted to Lorentz's dualistic theory, and we shall then consider the evolution of this theory and its relation to the theory of relativity.

The setting was henceforth matter and ether exploring their relationship through theories and experiments, top of which was the experiment of Michelson- Morley.

What is our image here?

it's quite blurry, like an image of non-zooming binoculars and we wait for the lens settings to see the landscape.

3.6   Electricity   and   motion,   the   negative experiments

Maxwell's equations were expressed in terms of a Cartesian coordinate system, that is they were referred to a definite rigid frame. Are there any restrictions on the choice of this frame? Maxwell does not seem to have paid much attention to this question, he believed that any frame one could reasonably choose, if he was willing to ignore –as indeed one must- experimentally indiscernible difference.

In Treatise 600 Maxwell argues that

"the electromotive intensity is expressed by a formula of the same type, whether we refer it to a fixed system of axes or to a system of axes moving with uniform linear and uniform angular velocity with respect to the former". Therefore "in all phenomena relating to closed circuits and the currents in them, it is indifferent whether the axes to which we refer the System be at rest or in motion. So much for the motion of conductors..**Maxwell**".

As to the ether, since the speed c with which electromagnetic action propagates through it is involved in Maxwell's equations, the equations obviously cannot take the same form with respect to any frame, whether the ether is at rest or in motion in it. Maxwell believed that any changes in their form arising from these considerations could be safely neglected, as they were still beyond the experimental detection.[27]

But ether theoretically looks like it wants to change the equations with its presence. The motion must detect its materiality, at least in terms of 19th century, *where everything moving is always material and vice versa.*

But there were many others experiments in the relation between motion of matter and electricity. For example the contraction of a solid transparent body, owing to it's motion through the ether, should give rise to phenomenon of double rerfaction, much as would follow from an ordinary physical

---

[27] In 1879, Clerk Maxwell wrote in DP Todd the U.S. Naval Observatory in Washington that examined the ability to calculate the speed of the solar system through the ether, by observing the eclipses of Jupiter's moons . Roemer, in the past, had used these measurements of time eclipse to measure the speed of light. Maxwell, however, concluded that the results sought were too small to measure - but the claim of the Maxwell noticed a young student of the Naval Academy , the Albert Michelson who was then transferred to this office. In 1878 at age 25 , the Michelson had made an excellent measurement of the speed of light, and he thought that the detection of motion through the ether could be measurable.

compression of the body. The experiment of Rayleigh and of Brace was base on this idea, but the result was a complete disappointment. The FitzGerald contraction gave rise to no such effect.

The experiment of **Trouton and Rankine** aimed to detect a variation in the electric conductivity of a strip of metal as a result of the FitzGerald contraction. Once more a negative result.

Another was suggested and carried out by **Trouton and Noble**. The essence of this experiment was based on the Rowland's phenomenon, that an electrified body in motion produces all the effects of an electric current. If therefore two electrified bodies were placed side to side the motion of the earth through the ether should produce two parallel electric currents; and since parallel electric currents attract one another, a very sensitive torsion balance shoul be able to detect the attraction; again the result was negative; the velocity of the earth through the ether evaded us completely.

Lorentz accepted what appeared to him as the inevitable, and asserted that the time had come to recognize that nature seem to have entered into some giant conspiracy to defraud us of a knowledge of our velocity through the ether. Accordingly, he laid down his celebrated **principle of cooperation**, (d'Abro) according to which adjustments were so regulated in nature that the velocity of our planet through the ether could never be detected, *however precise our experiments.*

3.7 Michelson-Morley experiment

The idea

Through the work of Maxwell, the optical ether of Cauchy, Fresnsel, Young, Larmor, Green, MacCullagh etc. meets electrodynamics theory, as electromagnetic fields are deformations and vibrations of ether of Maxwell, carrier of electromagnetic waves, which are identical with light waves. Now the optical phenomena are electromagnetic phenomena and any research on optical ether refers to the Maxwell electrical theory.

Although the mechanical models of the optical ether of Maxwell and Thomson were incomplete, the next generation of physicists accepts the ether described from the Maxwell equations as a peculiar kind of a physical being, different from the known material weighing system and perhaps more primary and fundamental despite the imperfect descriptions of it. The field electricity imposed an ether ghost in the plans of physicists, a metaphysical entity, beyond the realm of " *imperfect matter of senses.* "

> In a letter to Hertz of September 13th, 1889, Heaviside wrote:
>
> "....It often occurs to me that we may be all wrong in thinking of the ether as a kind of matter (elastic solid for instance) accounting for its properties by those of the matter in bulk with which we are acquainted; and that the true way, could we only see how to do it, is to explain matter in terms of the ether, going from the simpler to the more complex...."[28]

Now, the efforts of physicists to record some proof of the physical existence of this ether in nature, focused on the following considerations:

If there is a material medium of light propagation and thus of electromagnetic actions, must certifies it's existence in other ways besides propagation of light waves. e.g. we certify the existence of the air beyond the propagation of sound waves, from it's resistance to motion, from the effects of currents, etc. As an air stream varies the speed of sound, so the etheric stream will alter the speed of light, making it's presence felt. As the tendency of the fishing line increases when the boat is moving, as a result of materiality of water, so the electromagnetic actions will change, when the electrified bodies are moving in the sea of ether.

How is this translated to the mathematical model?

---

[28] Relativity and geometry Roberto Torretti page 38

The Galilean transformations, left invariant the equations of mechanics. This means that all inertial systems are equivalent to mechanics without any privileged. But the Galilean transformations alter the laws of Maxwell . When we apply a Galilean transformation on them, there appears a surplus of terms commensurate with the relative velocity u of systems, that does not exist in the original equations . This means that these laws - as admitted by classical science - retained their form in a single privileged inertial system and here for reasons of symmetry should be the system that is at rest in the stagnant ether. Thus the absolute velocity existed (the privileged system in nature) and had to be discovered. Otherwise we had to change the laws of Maxwell or the Galilean transformations!.

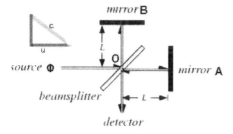

The experiment of Michelson Morley, is more widely known. A schematic diagram of the interferometer is given in Figure. The basic idea was to send two light beams from the source Φ to mirrors A and B (via the reflection of a mirror O for B) and return to O, whence they are further reflected into the detector, where interference fringes are observed as to the difference of the total time of each path , OAO and OBO. The path OA = L was in the direction of motion of the earth and OB = L perpendicular to the previous. According to the perception that the speed of light relative to the ether was c, composing the velocities of ether and light, it travels OB at a speed (relative the instrument) $\sqrt{c^2 - u^2}$ (u the velocity of earth relative to ether) classical composition of velocities as the river and the boat) so the time for the route OB+BO is

$$t_1 = \frac{2L}{\sqrt{c^2 - u^2}} = \frac{2L}{c\sqrt{1 - \dfrac{u^2}{c^2}}} \quad ....(1)$$

[113]

and for OA + AO

$$t_2 = \frac{L}{c-u} + \frac{L}{c+u} = \frac{2Lc}{c^2-u^2} = \frac{2L}{c(1-\frac{u^2}{c^2})} \quad \ldots\ldots\ldots\ldots(2)$$

Maxwell suggested that the two time lapses might be expected to differ by an extremely small amount and there was some doubt whether a sufficiently sensitive time measuring device, existed.

However **Michelson** applied his interferometer to the test of this suggestion.

The interferometer was sensitive enough to detect a time difference of this order, but the results were always less than predicted, the two runners with different speeds were reaching the end simultaneously. It was always that $t_1 = t_2$ which implies that u = 0, i.e. the earth was stationary in the ether, the result was zero![29]

3.8 The interpretation of Lorentz (the contracted electrons)

...In order to explain the absence of any effect on the earth's translation, I have ventured the hypothesis, which has also been proposed by Fitz Gerald that the dimensions of a solid body undergo slight changes , of the order of u^2/c^2 when it moves through the ether. (**Lorentz**, *the theory of electrons, page195*)

According to Lorentz, the non observation of this fringe shift is due to a contraction of the interferometer arm parallel to the "motion "through the

$$\sqrt{1-\frac{u^2}{c^2}}$$

---

[29] The experiment has been repeated many times since, first by Michelson and Morley in 1887 and later by D. C. Miller.

ether" axis, due to this motion. The Lorent coefficient acts therefore as an equalizer of the two altered light paths , capable of making both equal to

$$\frac{2L}{\sqrt{1-\frac{u^2}{c^2}}}$$

In this way a moving infer meter shows no fringe shift, even though this is not due to a true absent of affects, but to the interaction of two real distinct effects (the Lorentz contraction and the slowing of light speed) that partially compensate each other, making it impossible to detect their "sum" by means of an interferometer- the resultant is tropic alteration is then regarded by Lorentz as by convention dilated time. Thus in this contex, a real absence of effects (true null effect) could only occur at rest relative to ether.

So the length L alters (due to this contraction) and t_2 of the preceding relation (2) is

$$t_2 = \frac{2L}{c\sqrt{1-\frac{u^2}{c^2}}} = t_1$$

Finally, the null result of the experiment, namely the equality $t_1 = t_2$, is due to the interaction of two different real phenomena: **A.** the contraction of the length of the arm of instrument that is parallel to the "motion through the ether", which motion causes it **B.** the varying of speed of light in different directions with respect to the measuring instrument [30]

The length contraction is attributed from Lorentz, to mechanical causes and is real. A truly null effect would happen if the interferometer were really stationary relative to the ether.

> ... the size and shape of a solid body is determined by the
> molecular forces " and every cause that altered the latter will also

---

[30] The stability of c in the formulas 1 and 2 were evident for Lorentz, as in classical wave theory the wave velocity relative to the carrier of wave propagation is not dependent on the speed of the wave source, here the light source.

affect the shape and dimensions of the body. " This hypothesis is not subject to verification because we completely ignore the nature of the molecular forces , ... but if the dimensions of the electrons varied then field electrical forces would vary by the same amount, and assuming that the molecular forces also changed, then the impact on these of motion through the ether, will cause (this motion) a deflection equal to the requested size ..... **Lorentz**

The change therefore of the dimensions of the electron moving through the ether and the classical synthesis of velocities, is the basis of the interpretation. The mechanical force exerted by ether in anything that moves within, compresses the device of measuring in the amount just needed to cancel the result of the movement of the observer through the ether. This length's contraction of the length L_0 is described by

$$L = \frac{L_0}{\gamma}$$

$$\gamma = \frac{1}{\sqrt{1 - \frac{v^2}{c^2}}}$$

where L the observed length.

But the impacts of this force continue.

3.9 Lorentz transformations

Historically, the Lorentz transformation were discovered before the theory of special relativity. The idea was that Maxwell's equations only hold in the frame in which the aether is at rest; Lorentz proclaimed the ether at rest in absolute space. In principle this identifies the ether with absolute space.

The theory of transformations in Lorentz's theory has a different meaning from that of relativity. Here the transformations, link the measurements to the stationary ether system and to any inertial one, moving in space e.g. the ether and the earth in the MM experiment, with the idea, to manifest contraction of the bodies as moving through the ether. In relativity, they connect any two inertial systems in relative motion, - the ether has been

[116]

removed-, as a result of the *principle of relativity*. Then, they are called Lorentz-Einstein transformations.

Lorentz showed that measurements of position and time of an event, with a rod and a clock under this regime of etheric contraction, i.e. measurements that were in a system S′ moving with velocity υ relative to the system S fixed in ether, (in standard configuration) that is **observer comoving with the interferometer,** (to manifest contraction) would be different from Galilean measurements, they are

$$x' = \gamma (x - \upsilon t)$$
$$y' = y$$
$$z' = z$$
$$t' = \gamma (t - \upsilon x/c^2)$$

$$........(3.3)$$

with $\gamma = \dfrac{1}{\sqrt{1 - \frac{\upsilon^2}{c^2}}}$ and υ is the velocity of S′ as measured in universal

rest system of ether, S.

This common form of transformations in place of Galileans was introduced by Lorenz in 1904 to interpret the negative result of the experiment M.M by assuming the existence of a unique inertial system defined by the luminiferous ether, the system of ether, but a year later Einstein introduced these equations with the help of the principles of the new approach to the problem (principle of relativity). From these transformations we can us immediately extract the phenomena of time dilation (which Lorentz could not conceive, and Lorentz contraction. The length of any object in a moving frame relative to ether, will appear foreshortened in the direction of motion, or contracted. A clock in a moving frame in stagnant ether, will be seen to be running slow, or "dilated" according to the Lorentz transformation. But Lorentz assumed that these new transformations applied only to purely electromagnetic quantities, and no reference was made to their being applicable to mechanical phenomena as well.

[117]

What was the meaning of the new transformations? And even more of t´, which stipulated a different time in the moving system?

But the thriller with ether continues. Lorentz then showed the most important. The Maxwell equations remain unchanged in form if we apply to them the transformations Lorentz, (3) that as it was known is not valid for their respective Galileans. That is, the new transformations had the same characteristic relation to electromagnetics as Galilean transformations to Newtonian mechanics.

So the deception (so it seemed) of the moving observer is completed. Not only ripped off on measurements of space and time, but he believes that Maxwell 's equations are unchanged in a moving system in ether. That is no electromagnetic experiment could reveal the motion of the earth. And all these are based on mysterious contraction of bodies. This was real! The ether was there, material and present, but invisible since it negated our efforts to reveal it. Physicists thought so, but later ether became immaterial.

Einstein's interpretation

The Einstein introducing *the postulate of constancy of the speed of light* gives another interpretation of the experiment of Michelson-Morley. Since the velocities of light signals with respect the two arms is c, the duration of the two routes would be t=2L/c. So no time difference is detected! But even this axiom is an hypothesis as the interferometer measures the difference in the two routes, and we can not decide between zero phenomenon or a zero result, namely between two paths with equal durations 2L / c (Einstein) and two paths equal respectively with $L/\sqrt{1-u^2/c^2}$ (Lorentz). The difference is always zero!

Stoke's hypothesis

Another interpretation of a negative result would be the hypothesis of Stokes, the **ether drag hypothesis** dealt with the question whether the ether is dragged by or entrained within moving matter. Stokes assumed that bodies are transferring (dragging) the ether during their motion. That is the earth carries the ether as the atmosphere, so there is no ethereal stream that would alter the speed of light relative to the instrument of the experiment. Besides, if we had design a sound experiment to demonstrate the movement of the earth, an analogous experiment of M - M, the result would be negative. On the contrary sound experiments on a train platform, would prove it's motion, since the air is not transferred (dragged) by it.

But there 's another interpretation of the experiment .

That the result was …positive. The historical reference of Michelson, Morley on their experiment is[31]

".. …the actual shift (of the interference fringes) was clearly less than 1/20 of that (of the observed shift of the fringes) and probably less than 1/ 40 of this . But as the shift must be proportional to the square of the velocity , the relative velocity of the earth and the ether is probably less than 1/6 of the earth's orbital velocity , and certainly less than the ¼."

The experiment was later repeated from the D. C. Miller who spent many years with it. Always the result was less than expected, but not zero. The Miller insisted on the importance of small positive effect:

"Indeed a partial drag of the ether from the earth when moved, could affect the result, not to negate as would the total transfer (Case Stokes)".

But "however most experimenters and commentators of the experiment have concluded that the results show the impossibility of

---

[31] For further investigation of the matter Hector A. Munera, Michelson-Morley experiment revisited, systematic errors ... Apeiron Vo. 5 Nr. 1-2 January-April

detecting by electromagnetism, means the motion of the earth through
the ether...Robert Lindsay".

Other experiments designed during the early 1990's to detect the
motion of the earth through the ether, but failed to yield positive results of
anything like the expected magnitude, and this served to strengthen the general
conclusion that by electromagnetic means, cannot one detect motion with
respect to ether.

So in the (last) classical physicist Lorentz, the c varied without
repealed the ether, the motion deforms the bodies so it could not be revealed.
There is the "null result" of Lorentz in contrast with the "null effect" of
Einstein where c is a universal constant.

All experiments have shown that electromagnetic and optical
phenomena , relatively to the earth as the body of reference, are not
influenced by the translational velocity of the earth Einstein, the
meaning of relativity, 1921,p.29

So the state of the ether motion attributed to it by Lorenz (calmness)
was the conceptual contradiction that brought it's abolition through the MS
experiment, ending the long-term ether crisis that related to its nature and the
logical foundation of all electrical theory.

3.10 The end of classical electromagnetism: the field without ether is Aristotelian potentiality

The electromagnetic theory failed to explain one experiment, namely
the attempt to measure the relative motion of the earth though the hypothetical
all pervading ether.

Eventually physics decided to remove ether from the concepts of
physical reality, since they were not defined by visual experiments. It was a

conceptual judgment of electrical theory as ether was the carrier of electromagnetic phenomena. Now the field is an intangible reality! How did the natural community react to this cosmogony? References are abundant:

> The abandonment of the ether hypothesis leads to epistemological difficulties ... W. Wien
>
> .. physics without ether is not physics… .J. Stark
>
> .. ether is not a fantastic creation of a theoretical philosopher, it is as vital to us as the air we breathe. .J. Thomson
>
> … .It is now time to see that ether has played its historical role and deserves a place of honor only in the history of physics…. Frenkel

Larmor was the last British etherist. In the 1900s he claimed that matter can be, and probably is, a structure of ether but it is certain that ether is not a structure of matter.

> … Initially under the influence of Larmor at the turn of the century it was generally recognized that ether is an intangible medium, not composed of identifiable elements with definite positions in absolute space ... Whittaker

The transition from the "material" to the intangible non-mechanical field invokes many ideas and results in a loose distinction, the E and H vectors are not now ether modifications but excitations in space. For many, the intangible reality is weird as it is not an existence like the sea, the horse or the mountain.

> "Now, says Bateman, we have a difficult time getting a satisfactory picture of the processes that are generated or represented by vectors E and H."

So it is that for the majority of physicists the field is another reality even if it is not revealed to the senses.

> The physical side of science agrees to a large extent, and almost unanimously, that the torrent of knowledge is now directed to a non-mechanical truth. The universe is starting to look more like a big thought than a big machine… ..James Jeans

[121]

... Hidden behind the material that immediately reveals that there is from our senses, lies the field The discovery of the laws of the field and the laws by which this determines matter began with Maxwell's theory, and seems to go a long way. . But the existence of a substance has always been abandoned by our definitions of matter ... ...
Weyl (space, time, matter)

This is the Aristotle's dexcription of unobservable reality, of potentiality.

... .The material that our world is made of is mental material... .Eddington...

..The luminiferous ether of Kelvin, Maxwell, Faraday, after the results of the new look for the universe, can be described as dead. It is no longer a serious scientific affair, but simply an element of an anti-scientific dialect for popular descriptions... Jeans

... .An obsessive idea had occupied the minds of physicists. I am referring to the light ether... now that we are suddenly freed from this obsession, we feel as if we are awakened by a foul nightmare... .G.N.Lewis, the anatomy of science, 1926, p.75

The intangible field is behind the physical behaviour of the bodies, says Weyl. And Einstein's apostle, Minkowski writes:

.... In the development of mathematical conclusions there will be ample opportunities for experimental verifications that will persuade even those who have difficulty abandoning old established ideas, for the harmony that appears to exist between pure mathematics and physics... ..Minkowski.

It is the opposite of the operational view, Minkowski was not a physicist, he believes that the 'conceivable' in modern physical theory are provided by mathematical metaphysics, (Platonism) the electromagnetic field is a mathematical construct and it's 'pre-existing harmony', makes it real though not observable. The same thing happened with quantum mechanics: physicists did not care what was described by Schrödinger's equation,

[122]

probability or not, as long as the events of refraction or emission could be described with this monumental model.

Dirac is more "rigorous":

"The only object of theoretical physics is to calculate results that can be compared with experiment. It is completely unnecessary to describe the whole course of the phenomenon »The principles of quantum mechanics p.7

The theoretical physicist is now becoming the translator of mathematical relations,

... how can a relativist answer the question: how is light emitted if there is no medium for emission, and where, or where is the sun's radiation stored during the emission? It will simply answer that such a question can be asked by someone who has failed to appreciate our position on our view of the world of phenomena. In any case, even in the simplest of cases, the question cannot be answered in any way or why. Explanations never explain, they just describe... the very idea of explanation is beyond our perception, like the idea of creation. What we can only do is take things as we find them... F.R. Denton, Relativity and common sense 1924

That is, the science of physics contains nothing but quantitative description, viz equations. So, what does all this have to do, with dynamic lines of force, ether, field space, medium? these terms are the Aristotelian *phantasma, agents of human cognitive function* these do not fit into the formulas and can only be understood as virtual metaphors; these are our known images, are not meant as explanations but as the ghosts of the soul, to aid the intellect.

Things now look clean. As Newton's laws describe a mechanistic theory of matter, Maxwell's equations described a non-mechanistic theory of field. But, we are accustomed that, when we leave the mechanistic description everything .... is metaphysics, so we are accustomed to think of science only in mechanistic description. In this metaphysical description, the field is the Aristotelian potential reality of electromagnetics. It is the big image!Maxwell worked on potentiality with the only tool, the mathematical reasoning, and through this he saw the actuality, with models the old laws of electricity (Coulomb, Faraday, Ampere).

[123]

PART FOUR: ELECTROMAGNETICS AND RELATIVITY

introduction

Though the specific investigation of the special theory of relativity is beyond the scope of this book, it has already been found necessary to refer to Einstein's views. Any discussion of the ether would nowadays seem incomplete and faulty if the attitude of relativists to the problem were not at least recorded.

> ..the introduction of a "light ether" will prove to be unnecessary, since the view to be developed here does not require a "perfectly stationary space" endowed with special properties, nor does it impart a velocity vector to some point in the vacuum space where electromagnetic processes take place...Einstein 1905

We will see Einstein's description of the crucial and radical decision to resolve the long-standing crisis on the status of ether, the so-called **ether crisis.**

> "... Space-time theory and the kinematic theory of special space-time theory have been modelled on the Maxwell-Lorentz electromagnetic theory. This theory satisfies the conditions of the special theory of relativity but acquires a new aspect. Because if K is a reference system for which Lorentz's ether is at rest, the Maxwell-Lorenz equations apply primarily to the K system. But according to the special theory of relativity the same equations, without any change in their meaning, will apply to any new system K´ that moves in a uniform transport with respect to K. Now comes a critical question:

why should I in the theory distinguish the system K from all the above systems K´ which are equivalent to that of all opinions, supposing that the ether is at rest in relation to this system? For the theoretician such an asymmetry in the theoretical structure, without corresponding asymmetry in the field of experience is unbearable. Assuming that the ether is at rest in relation to K but in motion relative to K´, the physical equivalence of K and K´ seems to me logically not directly wrong but in any case unacceptable.The next place to deal with this state of affairs is the next: ether does not exist, there is nowhere. Electromagnetic phenomena are not modes of a medium and are not bound by any carrier, they are independent realities and do not reduce anywhere, just like the atoms of the weighing matter. This idea is the most fertile since, according to Lorentz's theory, electromagnetic radiation such as weighing matter transmits momentum and energy, and as according to the special theory of relativity, the two realities matter and radiation are forms of distributed energy, the weighing matter loses its isolation and appears as a particular type of energy ......

collected papers of Einstein »

The theory of special relativity plays an important role in the modern theory of classical electromagnetism. First of all, it gives formulas for how electromagnetic objects, in particular the electric and magnetic fields, are altered under a Lorentz transformation from one inertial frame of reference to another. By applying the transformation to all inertial frames of reference, he demonstrated that physics remained invariant as it had with the Galilean transformation, but that light was now invariant as well. Secondly, it sheds light on the relationship between electricity and magnetism, showing that frame of reference determines if an observation follows electrostatic or magnetic laws. Third, it motivates a compact and convenient notation for the laws of electromagnetism, namely the "manifestly covariant" tensor form.

Lorentz on his side continued to use the aether concept. In his lectures of around 1911 he pointed out that what "the theory of relativity has to say", "can be carried out independently of what one thinks of the aether and the

[125]

time". He reminded his audience of the fact that "whether there is an aether or not, electromagnetic fields certainly exist, and so also does the energy of the electrical oscillations" so that, "if we do not like the name of "aether", we must use another word as a peg to hang all these things upon." He concluded that "one cannot deny the bearer of these concepts a certain substantiality".

In view of the deadlock in the search for a mechanical model for the propagation of electromagnetic fields through space, Einstein was tempting to treat these fields as primary entities, sufficiently defined by the laws of their interdependence and ponderomotive action.

the two principles of theory are

A. Principle of Relativity of Motion:

All physical laws are covariant (invariant in form) for transitions from one inertial observer to another inertial observer.

This principle is that there is not ether. *All experiments run the same in all inertial frames of reference.*

B. the light postulate: **The speed of light is the same in all inertial frames of reference.** The light is propagated in the straight line, at the same constant velocity c in all directions and time periods, relative to each inertial system.

In fact, ether becomes an imaginary medium replaced by mathematical space-time. The meaning of the word relativity refers to the observations between two inertial systems in relative motion. These results are related to the Lorentz transformations,

"... Maxwell's fields are no longer material, they have been inoculated into charged electrons, forever rejecting the mechanistic philosophy from Descartes' time to W. Thomson, though they were born for mechanistic interpretations of electricity. ... Whitehead »

In electromagnetism there is a special characteristic: the classical vacuum electrodynamics, summarized in Maxwell equations, are form-invariant under a Lorentz transformation. It, was indeed this problem of

[126]

finding a transformation which leaves Maxwell equations unchanged, that led Lorentz to the discovery (1895) of the equations now associated with his name (Lorentz transformations). So relativity has little to contribute to the electromagnetic theory in vacuum in the way of new results. But it's four-dimensional viewpoint does add a new understanding as well as new techniques.

4.1 The transformations of E and B

The removal of ether eliminated the possibility of an executive detection of the Maxwell field. It will remain in physics as a creation of mathematical thought, which will later become involved with the great scientific overturns of special relativity and quantum physics.

With Einstein the field becomes four-dimensional and unobservable as thought. As though moves our arms, the field moves the charged bodies. It is mathematically transferred from system to system and there it exerts forces. Now it does not belong to material reality, it only fulfills the Maxwell equations and (as Newton used to say about the gravitational factor), let everyone understand it, as he can ..

..There is a fundamental difference between the electric field and a mechanical substance. The mechanical has a certain motion state ...but for the electric field there is no analogue picture ... we can imagine two observers in different vehicles cutting the electric field at different but relatively uniform speeds. Neither of them could claim that he alone was relatively calm about the electric field ......
.**Reichenbach,** Atom and Cosmos

... the electromagnetic field consists of "something" - physicists can say nothing more - which satisfies the Maxwell equations ... ..**B. Russel**

But it is decisive for the creation of the new space-time scenic for physical reality.

The elements of the relativistic description of electromagnetism are developed by mathematics of the four dimensions, where the mathematical treatment of the four-dimensional electric reality is made by the scalar magnitudes, the 4-vectors and the tensors. The basic four-vectors in relativistic electromagnetic theory is **the 4-vector of current density** $J\mu = (j, \rho)$, and **the 4-vector of potential** (A, φ). Even the **electromagnetic** η_{mn} with components E and H, where j, ρ, A, φ are known current and potential magnitudes related with the movement of currents and charges in our space and time. Now that they move in space-time - space and time have merged -, these sizes have been merged into a four-dimensional mathematical formalism that depicts a four dimensional unobservable reality.

The principle of relativity implies that the equation

$F = \{qE + qu \times B\}$.......(4.1) with u the velocity of charge as measured in S, will also apply to another S′ which moves at a uniform velocity υ in relation to S, having their common axis x. Then at S′

will apply $F' = \{E' + qu' \times B'\}$ ......(4.2)

So for example for y-component of F will have

$F_y = \{qE_y + q (u_z B_x x - u_x B_z)$ ....(4.3)

And for its y′ -component (F′)

$F_y' = \{qE'_y + q (u_z' B'_x - u'_x B'_z)$ ....(4.4)

We assume that (4.1) and (4. 2) refer to the same measurement act, so if the fields are measured at (x, y, z, t) in S and in (x′, y′, z′, t′) in S′ then the space and time coordinates will be associated with the Lorentz transforms.

Now with *relativistic transformations of 3-force and velocity u,* equations (4.3) and (4.4) are linked (their first members), giving the relations between the fields that summarized for all components in

$E_1' = E_1$ $(E_2' = E_2 - \upsilon/c\ B_3)$ $E_3' = \gamma\ (E_3 + \upsilon/c\ B_2)$....(4. 5a)

$B'_1 = B1$ $B'_2 = \gamma \left(B_2 + \frac{\upsilon}{c} E_3 \right)$ $B'_3 = \gamma(B_3 - \frac{\upsilon}{c} E_2$...(4.5.b)

[128]

They are the equations of transformation of the spatial dimensions of E and B in the formalism of relativity, from system to system, where E and H enter into the formation of a single tensor h_{mn}, the **electromagnetic tensor** h_{mn} (m, n are changed from 1 to 4). These show that the analysis of an electromagnetic field in in electric components and magnetic components has only a relative significance. In the space-time, the electric and magnetic fields "become simple shadows", resulting in the mixing of the electric and magnetic field and the birth of each one from the other as a result of the observer's movement. For example, a field that is either purely electric or purely magnetic in one system will generally have both electrical and magnetic components in another system.

But perhaps the most astonishing success of special relativity in electromagnetism is that it allows us to predict how electrical and magnetic fields are changed when we go from one system to another. For example, our experiment shows that an electron at rest is surrounded by an electrostatic field, while the same electron in relative motion is known to develop an additional magnetic field at right angles to the electrostatic. Before the discovery of Lorentz-Einstein's transformations, these experiments were noted but there was no interpretation to create the magnetic field with motion, just an empirical formula defined his birth and magnitude. With transformations, however, the problem cleared up. We achieved a theoretical interpretation of these mysterious events, and classical empirical formulas appeared only as approaches. It seemed that the electric and magnetic fields were no longer separate units but merely different aspects of the same entity - the electromagnetic tensor. Thus, the logical justification of the occurrence of a magnetic field around the electrified body in motion has been achieved: this field is a direct consequence of the changes of the fundamental types of space and time perception, changes that are expressed by the Lorentz transformations .

4.2 The electrodynamics of relativity

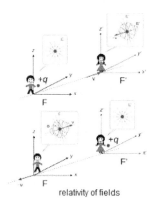

relativity of fields

"... how is it possible that the same body gives and at the same time does not give a magnetic field? In classical theory we had to interpret one of the two results as false. In the theory of relativity both are acceptable. The magnetic fields are relative .. **A. Eddington** »

The principle of relativity imposes strong constraints on every theory. In fact, Einstein's claim that as the Maxwell equations satisfy the principle of relativity, allowed him to achieve the transformation equations in the electric and magnetic fields.

Space-time is the new instrument of field electricity, a new explanatory image of electrical theory.

"To understand the significance of the new four-dimensional reality we have to think as follows: The relativistic method of solving a problem associated with a moving body, is to solve the problem for a body at rest and then to apply of the specific transformational equations to find the corresponding solutions for a body in motion **Compton and Allison p.759** "

The relativistic approach to the development of electrodynamics is based on the emergence of the close relationship between the experimental forces of electrical physics. It examines things as a function of the forces exerted between charges in different states of motion.

"... The Law of the Coulomb gives us the force exerted on the observation charge whatever its speed, provided the source charge is

[130]

stationary, while the magnetic force is associated with moving charges." (A.P.French)

The theory of relativity reveals the essential relationship between the Law of the Coulomb and the Laplace law of magnetic force. Here the distinction between rest and motion is not considered as fundamental (since the absolute motion has been abolished), as the distinction of phenomena due to moving or rest charges. This is a distinction that depends on a particular reference system. A source charge that moves in relation to a system and thus acts as a source of magnetic field in this system may be at rest relative to another system and therefore only generates an electric field on that system. This means (Einstein's fertile suspicion) that what appears to be a magnetic field in a reference system and exerts the magnetic force Laplace on a charge, can be an electric field when viewed from another system where it exerts on the same charge, the Coulomb force ..

this is the deepest consequence of the prin ciple of relativity, in electric theory.

So based on the Coulomb law alone we can achieve a quantitative description of the electromagnetic interactions between moving charges at arbitrarily constant speeds (A.P.French)"

Let's look at the two interpretations by Einstein himself:

"1. If a unit electric point charge is in motion in an electromagnetic field, there acts upon it, in addition to the electric force, an "electromotive force" which, if we neglect the terms multiplied by the second and higher powers of v/c, is equal to the vector-product of the velocity of the charge and the magnetic force, divided by the velocity of light. (Old manner of expression, Lorentz)

2. If a unit electric point charge is in motion in an electromagnetic field, the force acting upon it is equal to the electric force which is present at the locality of the charge, and which we ascertain by transformation of the field to a system of co-ordinates at rest relatively to the electrical charge. The analogy holds with "magnetomotive forces." (New manner of expression.)...

[131]

The analogy holds with "magnetomotive forces.

" We see that electromotive force plays in the developed theory merely the part of an auxiliary concept, which owes its introduction to the circumstance that electric and magnetic forces do not exist independently of the state of motion of the system of co-ordinates. Furthermore it is clear that the asymmetry mentioned in the introduction as arising when we consider the currents produced by the relative motion of a magnet and a conductor, now disappears. Moreover, questions as to the "seat" of electrodynamic electromotive forces (unipolar machines) now have no point". **Einstein 1905"**

In the classical formula of Lorentz, B was stable in space, but the charge without velocity (u= 0) did not interact with it. Now in the new interpretation, B does not exist in one system and occurs in the other, as a result of the relative movement of the systems, the other system is another field, magnetism is the result of the relative motion of the reference systems.

The principle of relativity is the physical cause of these results. The mathematical cause is the Lorentz transformations. In the electrical processes referred to in system S′, vectors E and H become E′ and H′. But the fields as defined, are not transported by a physical process, but are transformed. Mathematical transformations, -that come from the principle of relativity-, is like to contain condensed physical processes, it seems like mathematics to be thought experiments. We speak here for a non-observable reality, that its operational definition refers to its consequences.

So what is the point where we introduce physics into the general theory that Bridgman asks? **It is the old electrical forces within the new space-time frame**, the Coulomb force in a succession of media, geocentrism (Aristotle), absolute space (Newton), ether (Poincare′) space-time (Einstein, Minkowski), finally, with a new principle of relativity.

Now knowing the types of field transformation we can define the fields of a charge moving at a uniform velocity, starting from the Coulomb formula in an inertial system where the charge is at rest.

[132]

Example: We now consider the problem of calculating the mechanical force **f** that 'senses' a charge e, moving at velocity υ in the void space through an electromagnetic field E and H where the measurements refer to a given system S. Let S′ the system of rest of the charge at the time of the problem and the coordinates of the two systems are in standard configuration. Then the force **f**′ acting on the charge at S′ the Coulomb's force is given **by   f′ = e E′**

or

$$f_1' = eE_1' \qquad f_2' = eE_2' \quad f_3' = eE_3' \ \dots\dots\dots (4.6)$$

where E is the electric field in S.

By substituting the prime letters of (4.6) by (4.5) and the types of force and assuming that in our case $\upsilon = u$, (attention) still the rest mass of the particles of charge remains constant (for the transformation of force) we have for the system S

$$f_1 = eE_1 \quad f_2 = e(E_2 - \frac{uH_3}{c}) \quad f_3 = e(E_3 + \frac{uH_2}{c}) \quad \dots(4.7)$$

We can write (4.7) in a single equation of vector form

$$f = q \ \{E + (u \times H)\}$$

classical formula was the velocity of the particle relative to the absolute reference system, the ether.

That is, the classical Lorentz force now refers to any inertial system[32].

In classical theory it was a necessary fifth postulate besides Maxwell's four equations. But in relativity, the formula   appears as theorem. Because Lorentz could not at the time understand the relativistic transformations of the 3-force, or velocity, where were based the equations 4.5.

This is the electromagnetism of relativity, where we see that

"... we consider the forces to be a primary issue. Verification of the electric and magnetic field is then a secondary step, based on the analysis of the total force in parts independent of the velocity of the

---

[32] Rindler W.(1969) *special relativity* OLIVER AND BOYD EDINBURG NEW YORK

observation charge (field E) and dependent on the velocity of the observation charge (field B). (**A.P.French**) »

Thus, Maxwell's work, together with Einstein's special relativity theory, constituted a unification of the electric and magnetic fields into a more meaningful electromagnetic field. Of course Maxwell's equations, as saw above, still refer to the electric and magnetic fields separately. The complete mathematical unification of these fields came a little later, from the beautiful work of Hermann Minkowski, when he introduced the *Maxwell tensor* (or *Maxwell bivector*) into the theory in 1908. This mathematical object has six degrees of freedom, representing the three components of each of the electric and magnetic fields and which, owing to its *tensor* nature, could be regarded as being, in a well-defined sense, independent of the observer. However, a particular observer may still retrieve his personal electric and magnetic fields from it, by a simple procedure. Maxwell's equations may then be rewritten in a simple and elegant way as differential equations involving this tensor.

But as we already know, Maxwell's equations were covariant with Lorentz transformations. So here, beyond the use of a new formalism, there are no deadlocks and surprises like mechanics.

Maxwell's theory is relativistic correct.

Einstein so, does not appear to be concerned with anything more about the field, than the mathematical consequence of the equations. Although he states that the experiment alone controls the correctness of a theory, it has always believed that mathematical beauty rather than experiment, could in itself indicate the right direction for scientists. Einstein's great ability was to give physical interpretations of mathematical phenomena. The mathematical effect in the case of the field, was the covariance of the Maxwell equations as to Lorentz transformations. This was meaning something about nature.....

So special relativity eventually rescue the Maxwell field. Maxwell's equations were designed as if to fulfill Einstein's office. On the other hand,

[134]

four-dimensional formalism covers the logical gaps of the theory of motion, of system-to-system transfer, of the M-M experiment.

Epilogue.

This final image of electromagnetism is mathematical, is like an abstract painting. It is a mathematical picture, far from any intuition, it has a mathematical framework in place of ethereal, the space- time, that is ultimately translated into space and time to reach in our experimental verifications.

Asked if he believes in the four dimensions, Einstein answered:

"I believe, but in an abstract way. It's the way we think. The human mind is incapable of seeing and expressing images in four dimensions - not even in electricity. That does not mean, of course, that they are any less real than electricity, the power that controls our Universe and in which we owe our existence".

The discovery of Lobatchevski's geometry, is a radical departure from the older notion that mathematics asserts "absolute truths", a notion that was destroyed once and for all by the discovery of Non-Euclidean geometry. In fact this freedom of axioms may account for the great increase in the abstractness and generality of modern mathematics. Then everything in mathematics, physics, even in art, became abstract.

The deeper we get into nature, the more mathematical and abstract it becomes. One would say that the "medium" of electrical interaction imposed the new space-time framework. Seeking to define ether operationally, we found the space-time, and at the same time the ether became a mathematical "field". But this field remains not visualized by the layman…

APPENDIX

1.Weber force vs Lorentz force

The main difference between these two expressions is that Weber's force is completely relational. By the term relational we mean any force that depends only on the relative distance, velocity, acceleration, derivative of the acceleration, etc., between the interacting bodies. Lorentz's force, on the other hand, depends on the velocity of the test charge relative to the observer and not on the relative velocities between the test charge and the charges with which it is interacting. Another difference is that while Weber's force is symmetrical in the velocities and accelerations, the same does not happen with Lorentz's force.

While Weber's force always complies with the principle of action and reaction, the sanle does not happen in general with Lorentz's force, but only in some very specific cases and symmetrical situations.

Another major difference between Weber's electrodynamics and classical electromagnetism is that we do not need to talk about fields with Weber's force. The only things that matter are the charges, their distance, relative velocities, and relative accelerations. The electromagnetic fields may be introduced in Weber's electrodynamics but only as mathematical constructs without any physical reality. On the other hand, in Maxwell electromagnetism the fields are all important. They are the inter - mediate agents between the charges, they carry energy and moment, after their generation they exist independent of the charges, etc

In the Appendix we see a comparison of the three treatments.

<u>Two charges moving with the same velocity</u>

[136]

Let e and e′ have the same velocity υ with respect to the system S, parallel to the axis O. For t = 0, let the line joining them be identified with the axis Oy.

According to Lorentz's formula the force in e is

F = e [E + υ / c × B], where υ is the velocity of the charges relative to the ether

It is $eE = ee'\frac{ee'}{r^2}\vec{y}_0$

$B=(Biot\text{-}Savart)=\frac{e\,'\upsilon}{cy^2}$ in the direction of Oz

and $\upsilon/c{\times}B= -\,e\upsilon^2/c^2\,y^2\,y_0$

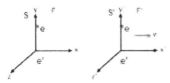

So the final force in e on S system είναι

$$F = \frac{ee\,'(1-\upsilon^2)}{y^2}y_0 \quad (1)$$

Weber force is simpler. Since the relative radial velocity of the two electrons is zero, the force between them is the known Coulomb force in any system, hence in S so

$$F_w=[ee\,'/y^2]\,y_0 \ldots\ldots\ldots\ldots\ldots\ldots(2)$$

which has been verified by delicate experiments.

In relativity theory, the domains in the two systems are related to known transformations. We consider the system S moving at velocity U with respect to S, where the loads are stationary so the force in it is the Coulomb force. Transforming the original system, the force between the electrons is given by it

$$F_{\sigma\chi} = \sqrt{1-\frac{\upsilon^2}{c^2}}ee'/y^2y_0\ldots\ldots\ldots(3)$$

The difference between (3) and the Weber force (2) is negligible for small values of u. But U is not conceptually the same. In Weber power there is no speed, their relative speed is zero. In classical force (1) u is the velocity relative to the ether system S is selected as ether stationary, but in the relative force (3) u is the velocity of the charges relative to any inertial reference system.

"There is not a single experimental verification that this force is other than the Coulomb force. We have to look elsewhere for 1 or 3 verification. "A. O' Rahily

BIBLIOGRAPHY

A.d' Abro (1950): the evolution of scientific thought from Newton to Einstein *Dover Publications*

Ampere, Mem. De l'Acad. VI (1825)

T. Assis. A.Koch (1962): Weber's electrodynamics Springer – Science+Business Media B.V

A.K.T Assis, J.Fukai, H.B.Carvallo,(2000) *"Weberian induction"* Physics letters, A.268

P. Bridgman (1927) *The logic of modern physics* New York Mackmillan

P. Cornille (2003) *Advanced electromagnetism and vacuum Physics*, World Scientific Publishin Co. France

E.G. Cullwick,(1957) *Electrodynamics and relativity*, Longmans, Green and CO.

O. Darrigol (2000) *Electromagnetism from Ampere to Einstein*
Oxford Univeriry Press

P.C.W.Davies (1986): *forces in nature* Cambridge University Press

Δ.Δαγκλής (2001): *ο συμβατισμός του Duhem και η επίδρασή του στο λογικό Εμπειρισμό*

P.M.M. Duhem (1991): *the aim and structure of physical theory*
Princeton University Press (διαδίκτυο τελευταία πρόσβση 25/8 2016)

A.Einstein (1905): *on the electrodynamics of moving bodies*
Ελληνική μετάφραση Γιώργος Μπαντές www.mpantes.gr

M.Faraday (18440): *experimental researches in electricity* volume
London

R.Fynman (1988): *QED* Τροχαλία

A.P.French: *ειδική θεωρία σχετικότητας* Εκδόσεις Αναγέννησις ,
Κων. Θεοχαρίδης, μετάφραση Παπαγιαννακόπουλος, Μεταξάς

J. Fukai (2003) : A promenade along electrodynamics Vales Lake
Publishing L.L.C

P. Graneau(1985): *Ampere -Neumann Electrodynamics of
Metals*(Hadronic Press,Nonantum, MA

D. J. Griffiths *(1999):Introduction to Electrodynamics.* Upper Saddle
River, NJ: Pearson Prentice Hall, 3rd edition.(Στα Ελληνικά 2005, εκδόσεις
Κρήτης)

W.Heisenberg (1958*): Physics and philosophy* Harper and Brothers
N.Y.

Hertz H. (1956) *the principles of mechanics* N.Y. Dover

O.Heaviside(1912):*electromagnetic theory* London

H. Helmholtz,(1872) *Philosophy Magazine xliv, 530* .

R.B.Lindsay *(1969) Concepts and methods of theoretical physics*:
Dover Publications.

G.H.Livens (1926): theory of electricity Cambridge

H.A.Lorentz, (1909) *Theory of electrons* Leipzig

C. W. Lucas, Jr. and **J. C. Lucas**, (2003) *"Weber's Force Law for Finite-Size Elastic Particles," GalileanElectrodynamics, Vol. 14,*

J. C. Maxwell (1904) *A Treatise on Electricity and magnetism* : Oxford

Παπαδημητράκη – Χλίχλια Ι.Α. Τσουκαλάς (1987)   Ε. *Ηλεκτρομαγνητισμός*: Εκδόσεις Ζήτη.

L.Page (1922): *introduction on electrodynamics* Boston

T. Phipps (1986): *Heretical Verities*, Urbana III ClassicNon-fiction Library

J.Piley (1933) :*electricity*, Oxford

M.Planck (1932) : theory of electricity and magnetism London

C.Pollack, D. Stump (2002) *Foundations of electromagnetic theory* Addison Wesley publishing company

A. O' Rahily. (1965)*Electromagnetic Theory* : Dover Publications Inc. New York

W.Rindler (1969): *Special relativity,*   Oliver and Boyd Edinburg Interscience Publishers Inc.N.Y

W.G.V Rosser (1991) *introductory special relativity,* Taylor&Francis N.Y

A.Shadowits (1988): Special Relativity Dover Publications N.Y

H. C. Slater and Nathaniel H. Frank (1969): *Electromagnetism,* Dover Publications Inc. New York

L. Solymar (1976) *Lectures on Electromagnetic theory* Oxford University press

A. Sommerfield : *Electrodynamics* ,   Academic Press New York and London

R.Torretti (1996): *Relativity and geometry*, Dover Publication, Inc. N.Y

W. Weber (1872) Εκτο υπόμνημα που η Αγγλική του μετάφραση βρίσκεται στο Philosophical Magazine 4th series Vol.43 No 283 January 1872pp1-20, 119-49

E. Whittaker *A(1960) history of the theories of Aether and Electricity:* , Harper Brothers , New York

F.Wilczeck (2008): *Η ελαφρότητα του είναι,* Εκδόσεις Κάτοπτρο

Assis, AKT; HT Silva (September 2000). *"Comparison between Weber's electrodynamics and classical electrodynamics". Pramana. 55 (3): 393–404*

Assis, AKT; JJ Caluzi (1991). "A limitation of Weber's law". Physics Letters A. 160 (1): 25–30.

Wesley, JP (1990*). "Weber electrodynamics, part I. general theory, steady current effects". Foundations of Physics Letters. 3 (5): 443–469*

Electromagnetic theory O'Rahily (1965)

Concepts and methods of theoretical physics R.B.Lindsay (1969)

A history of the theories of ether and electricity E.Whittaker (1960)

Theory of electron's A.Lorentz (1909)

Το φαινόμενο του ηλεκτρισμου Γιώργος Μπαντές www.mpantes.gr

Rindler W.(1969) *special relativity* OLIVER AND BOYD EDINBURG NEW YORK

Ειδική θεωρία σχετικότητας A.P.French, εκδόσεις Αναγέννησης

Special relativity in the shadow of geometry, George Mpantes Lambert Publications

THE END

Printed in Great Britain
by Amazon

87275695R10088